THE

Memorial Public Library

OF

ALEXANDRIA, PA.

DISCARD

Class ___j551.5__ Number ___Bi____

SKYWATCHERS
The U. S. Weather Bureau in Action

OTHER BOOKS
by WILLIAM BIXBY

MCMURDO, ANTARCTICA
HAVOC
The story of natural disasters

THE RACE TO THE SOUTH POLE

THE IMPOSSIBLE JOURNEY
of Sir Ernest Shackleton

SKYWATCHERS

The U. S. Weather Bureau in Action

by

William Bixby

Decorations by YUKIO TASHIRO

Photographs from the Weather Bureau

DAVID McKAY COMPANY, INC.

New York

SKYWATCHERS

COPYRIGHT © 1962 BY WILLIAM BIXBY

All rights reserved, including the right to reproduce
this book, or parts thereof, in any form, except for
the inclusion of brief quotations in a review.

PUBLISHED SIMULTANEOUSLY IN THE DOMINION OF CANADA

FIRST EDITION SEPTEMBER 1962
REPRINTED JUNE 1964

LIBRARY OF CONGRESS CATALOG CARD NUMBER: 62–16715

MANUFACTURED IN THE UNITED STATES OF AMERICA

Acknowledgment

The author would like to acknowledge his appreciation for the help freely given by the men of the U. S. Weather Bureau to make this book possible. Special thanks are due: Mr. Walter Hattman and his colleagues at the Caribou, Maine, Weather Station, Mr. Silvio Simplicio and his forecasters at Idlewild Airport; several unknown but nonetheless helpful meteorologists at the National Meteorological Center and at the Washington Headquarters of the Bureau who read the manuscript and made many helpful suggestions.

Special thanks are due to the U. S. Dept. of Commerce, Weather Bureau, for photographs on plates 1, 2, 3, 5, 6, 7, 8, and the U. S. Navy for official photograph on plate 4.

W.B.

Dedication

to

BERTHA L. GUNTERMAN

Whose love of good books
transcends everything

Contents

List of Illustrations

SKYWATCHERS

The U. S. Weather Bureau in Action

CHAPTER I

Station Caribou

At 4:00 a.m. one August 22nd, rain began to fall on the streets and buildings of Caribou, Maine. Streetlights shone on the glistening pavement. Rain drifted down in the cones of light. It looked like smoke. Water washed the dusty, wide streets of the town. It gurgled down the drains at the corner of Main and Sweden streets. The stores in the central business section were dark but a night-light burned in the Northern National Bank and its guardian beam wavered and shifted behind the curtain of falling water. The marquee of the Caribou Theater loomed white in the darkness. No lights shone in the IGA store or the Currier Furniture store but across the street from these buildings the Victory Restaurant was ablaze with light. Fluorescent bulbs behind the glass-fronted exterior cast their harsh glare on the counter where several truck drivers leaned, sipped coffee, and stared at the wall. A dark-haired waitress filled the coffee urn, pouring water from a pitcher methodically. The restaurant door opened and another waitress entered, her white apron showing beneath the skirt of her raincoat. Water ran from her shoes, darkening the floor around her. She shook her head and brushed at her tousled hair with one hand.

"Whew," she said, "it sure is raining. It woke me up, that's what it did."

The truck drivers turned their heads and stared at her and then at the windows where raindrops pelted the glass. There was no doubt about it. It was raining. None of the truck drivers spoke. All knew they'd be delayed driving the loads of new potatoes south to the Boston and New York markets. If the rain stopped, they might be able to make up some of the time. If it didn't, they would arrive late.

The waitress who was filling the coffee urn put down the heavy pitcher and looked at the new one. "You're early," she said.

The girl shook her raincoat vigorously and smiled, nodding. "Yeah. I couldn't sleep. The rain. It woke me up."

A thousand feet above the Victory Restaurant, nimbostratus clouds moved through the darkness over the silent, sleeping land. They came from a northwesterly direction. The wind that bore them was a chill 55°F and moved at fifteen miles an hour.

A police car cruised slowly toward the outskirts of Caribou, its wheels throwing up arcs of water that gleamed in the reflection of the headlights. The car's windshield wipers waved frantically trying to keep the glass clear. At the edge of town the police car turned back. Beyond lay thousands of acres of potato plants, soaked by the rain, surrounding the dark farm buildings.

By 4:30 lights had come on in the farmhouses. Farmers

rubbed calloused fingers through sleep-tousled hair and then tugged high farm shoes on their feet. They went to their kitchens and snapped on the lights, lit the gas beneath the coffee, turned on the radio. The kitchens in most of the farmhouses were neat and had the latest model refrigerators, stoves, freezers, dishwashers. The houses themselves and the barns were painted, well cared for. Aroostook County is large and prosperous. It is as large as Connecticut and Rhode Island combined, and is prosperous because of its potatoes. Nearly one of every seven potatoes grown in the United States comes from this northern Maine county. A hundred-acre potato farm can make a man prosperous. A combination of three or four such farms can make him wealthy—if the potatoes grow well and the weather stays good . . . Outside the farmhouses the rain fell on the rows of luxuriant potato plants that reached far across the land.

The farmers sipped coffee and waited for breakfast. They paid little attention to the all-night disc-jockey tunes that filled the kitchens with mournful sounds. Only when the music stopped did they listen for the early morning forecast. How long would the rain continue? Would there be too much? They'd had a good growing summer so far. But if the weather . . .

Less than a mile north of the center of Caribou where Sweden Street crosses Main Street, which is U.S. Route #1 through the town, is the Caribou Municipal Airport. Inside its gates lies a square white concrete building topped by a plastic-covered hemisphere. Beyond this peculiar structure is the single hangar. On its north and west sides many light planes stood, tied to stakes driven into the earth. The rain splashed on their wings and the wind coming from the northwest whined through the struts and made the planes quiver. On the northwest corner of the hangar a rectangular room, jutting from beneath the corner of the larger curved roof, blazed with light. On the door at the west end of the room was lettered:

U.S. WEATHER BUREAU AIRPORT STATION, CARIBOU, MAINE.

It is the northernmost station in the eastern United States and Americans know it chiefly, if they know it at all, as one which, from time to time, reports the lowest temperatures in the country. To Weather Bureau officials in Washington, Caribou is simply one of more than six hundred stations operating around the clock, seven days a week, gathering data about the weather. To citizens of Aroostook County, it is the source of all they know about the weather—what it is, what it was, and what it is going to be.

Oblivious of this monumental responsibility, the weatherman standing the night watch inside the station leaned on the counter and studied the latest weather map. Occasionally he glanced at the preceding maps stacked beneath the present one and from time to time jotted notes on a blank pad near his hand. His primary problem at the moment was to compose an early forecast. Boston usually gives the earliest New England forecast at 6:00 A.M. but the farmers of Aroostook County are impatient.

Above the endless chatter of the teletypewriters came the shrill ringing of the phone. The night man heard it even above the radio music blaring into the room from the Presque Isle station a few miles to the south. The weatherman made a last note and went to answer it. He knew the call would be from the Presque Isle station, WAGM, asking for the early weather so farmers would know what to expect and truck drivers could judge their schedules and speed.

In the farmhouse kitchens the farmers listened. In the Victory Restaurant the truck drivers who remained put down their cups and strained to hear, wishing the waitresses would stop talking.

"Cloudy and cool with rain or drizzle this morning, becoming partly cloudy to cloudy with a few scattered showers this afternoon, tonight and Wednesday and not much change in temperature. High today 63 to 68, low tonight 53 to 58. High Wednesday 65 to 70. Northeasterly winds 10 to 20 miles per hour today gradually becoming northwesterly and diminishing tonight. Northwest 10 to 15 miles per hour on Wednesday."

When the weatherman heard the announcer read the information, he returned to the weather map and gave it another look. He turned back the sheet containing the weather at the earth's surface and studied the upper-air map, called the 500-millibar map, where the atmospheric pressure is approximately half of what it is on the surface. On this map great weather systems over the entire United States can be seen at a glance. His map showed a large low-pressure area centered over the Midwest. The lines of equal pressure, called isobars, formed closed curved lines about the middle of this huge system. Their northern edges reached into Canada and their southern rims arced over the Gulf of Mexico. The weatherman studying it let his eye move along the isobars coming up the eastern side of the low-pressure area from the Gulf. They crossed the cotton lands of east Texas, the rivers and bayous of Louisiana and moved northward across the red-clay country of north Georgia and Arkansas, over the deep, narrow valleys of Tennessee and across the Appalachians to the small, neat, fenced farms of Pennsylvania, then curving westward across the flinty ground of northern New York and the dark spruce forests of southern Canada. The low-pressure system would bring moisture all the way from the Gulf to Aroostook County. The weatherman didn't doubt that, but he knew it wouldn't arrive for a day or two. His gaze went to a small low-pressure cell straddling the U.S.-Canadian border on the western side of Aroostook County. It had moved rapidly from its last position and it was the cause of the rain that still came down on the planes and the runways and the roof of the weather station itself.

The sky lightened in the east. In Caribou a few cars rolled down Sweden Street. Truck drivers settled themselves into their cabs and the engines roared to life. The farmers walked out of the kitchens, through the mud to the barns.

The waitress who had come in early stood by the window, peering through the rain at the lighter sky and the dark clouds. She turned, with her hands on his hips, and said, "Gee, I wonder when it's gonna stop raining."

She hadn't listened to the radio.

At the airport weather station, the night man poured the last of the coffee into a thermos cup and sipped it thoughtfully. It was five. He had a lot to do. He filled in the hourly report and machine punched the data in code on a small strip of paper tape which he then placed in the teletypewriter. He didn't have to send the message. When the central office for his district wanted the information, they would press the proper button to start transmission automatically and the data from Caribou would go out over the circuit to all the stations.

The weatherman stepped outside the office and pulled the door shut behind him. He looked up at the sky. The lowest layer of clouds was broken in places. Above it, through the openings, he could see higher, lighter clouds—altostratus—reflecting dimly the light from the obscured morning sun. The eastern horizon was the lightest portion of the sky. Below the low, dark nimbostratus and above the undulating line of hills, a band of whiteness marked the beginning day. Oblivious of the rain that drove across the runways and soaked earth around the hangar, the skywatcher walked stolidly to the white concrete shelter near the gate. The hemisphere on top of it gleamed dully. He unlocked the door of the building and stepped into the cube-shaped interior, shivering a little. The wind was chilly and he hadn't bothered to put on his jacket or raincoat. He carried a folded black rubber balloon. Once inside, he fixed it to a gas nozzle connected by rubber tubing to one of dozens of helium-filled tanks that more than half filled the room. Selecting a particular weight from a number on the table, he hung it on the nozzle and turned the valve. Except for the wind rattling the door and the slap of rain outside, the only sound was the hiss of gas as it inflated the balloon. The shape grew nearly spherical and the great black ball hovered in the air above his head. When enough gas entered the balloon to lift the nozzle and its weight an inch or two above the table top, he turned off the valve and tied the neck of the balloon with a piece of cord. Then he walked outside, released the balloon and glanced at his wristwatch as he did. The balloon rose rapidly.

A chip of wood released from the bottom of a pool of water will rise at a regular rate through the liquid medium. That rate is determined by the size and kind of wood employed. So a balloon will rise through the fluid medium of the air at a known rate if filled with a particular amount of gas. The amount the skywatcher used was just enough to make the balloon ascend at the rate of a thousand feet a minute. He stood, head tilted back, watching the balloon, its dark shape silhouetted against the gray clouds. It moved away from the station traveling toward the southeast but mounting at a constant rate toward the heavens. It grew smaller in his sight and began to disappear as it entered the lowest torn fringes of the clouds. He waited until it vanished and then checked his watch. Just one minute had elapsed. The cloud base lay a thousand feet above the station.

In addition to the six-hourly weather reports making up the general weather map on the surface, airport station weathermen must gather information for pilots. Of great importance to any pilot approaching a field such as Caribou on such a day as this is the ceiling and visibility. These were, at the moment, satisfactory: a thousand-foot ceiling and at least fifteen miles visibility to the hills and peaks of mountains visible south and east of the town.

Going back to the station, the weatherman didn't pause to glance at the whirling cups of the anemometer or the wind vane atop the hangar. But when he got inside he read the dials set in one wall and saw at a glance both wind speed and direction. He paused to fill in the information on the sheet for the benefit of pilots and then turned his attention to the next chore —preparing for an upper-atmosphere sounding. He could not do the job alone but he could ready the instruments for the men who were even now rising from their sleep at home or eating breakfast, thinking about the station and the condition of the weather. Average citizens, too, were thinking about the weather but scarcely in the same way. To most people the weather is either good or bad—and anyway it will change. To the men whose life business it is to watch the sky, the gusts of wind and the driving rain brought to mind pictures of the last weather map they had seen the day before, the words of the forecasts made in the preceding twenty-four or thirty-six hours which were being proved true or in error at the moment.

Few people know the formidable task these watchers of the sky face. The forces that rule and move the atmosphere are beyond most laymen's comprehension. In one year, for example, the energy of the winds blowing across 40°N latitude is equivalent to two billion atomic bombs or, put another way, equals the entire output of electrical energy of the United States at its present level for a time of 3000 years. In one storm which struck New York City in February, 1961, forty million tons of snow fell on the hapless city. Citizens, who seldom really see the sky or try to understand it, offered many angry solutions to the problem of the snow-clogged streets. One perennial suggestion is to melt the snow rather than trying to cart it away. But to do that would require—in the case of this storm—the heat equivalent of 120 atomic bombs.

Station Caribou is one of more than sixty stations in the United States gathering data on upper-atmospheric conditions —data which when processed results in a series of maps at various pressure levels above the earth which gives forecasters another dimension to watch and measure each day. The night man, still alone in the station room, began preparations for the morning sounding.

From a cardboard container he took a small white plastic

box and opened one end. A radio transmitter was fixed firmly to one end of the box. He took a small battery and went to the washroom and filled the bowl with water, then dunked the battery in it for fifteen seconds. Walking into the station room he shook the battery, removing excess water, and then fitted it into the niche reserved for it next to the transmitter. He connected the leads, inserting the ceramic-coated temperature-measuring wires and adjusted the humidity indicator. Then he placed the whole contraption in a wooden box, closed the door and turned on a small fan. The transmitter began to function and he turned to the two army-surplus recording machines standing in one corner of the room. Prior to preparing the transmitter he had switched on the receiving machines and given them time to warm up. Now, with the transmitter only a few feet from the receivers, he checked the machines for accuracy of recording the data which would appear on a long roll of graph paper as small marks made at precise spots between the numbered lines. The recording pen of the receiver shuttled first to the right and then to the left, dipping down to register a mark at the end of each journey. He made several small adjustments—the marks had to be right on the target, for an error in such recording of 10 per cent in the humidity at high altitude could change the shape of the weather map that would be drawn from the information. He checked the humidity in the wooden box where the transmitter sat. A fan blowing air around in the box evaporated moisture from a pan of water set at the bottom. Within minutes after the box was closed, the air became saturated and the transmitter signaled 100 per cent humidity.

Satisfied at last with the machines' adjustments, he turned

off the receivers, took the transmitter from the box and hung it on a nail outside the door so it would adjust to actual surface conditions.

The two machines are esssentially a radio receiver connected to a graph paper recording mechanism. The other machine is electrically connected to a large radio direction-finding antenna housed in the hemisphere atop the inflation shelter by the gate. The antenna, which also is army surplus equipment, was designed for field use. It sits on a tripod base on the concrete roof, sheltered from flying dust and errant birds by the hemisphere enclosing it. The saucer-shaped antenna can be rotated both vertically and horizontally by manually governed electric motors from within the station or set on automatic tracking by the flick of a switch. The information obtained from this machine is translated into the wind speed and direction at desired altitudes.

The door of the station room opened. A member of the morning watch came in and greeted his "dead man's shift" colleague. Together the two men went to the inflation shelter and allowed 2800 grams of helium to fill a large white balloon. When the neck of it was tied, a long cord was attached and the transmitter, or radiosonde, with a parachute above it, was attached. When released, the balloon would rise at the rate of a thousand feet a minute and each minute the transmitter would send back messages received in the station room on the two instruments. At some altitude near 100,000 feet the balloon would burst in the thin air of the upper atmosphere and the transmitter, its mission completed, would drift to earth beneath the parachute. Where it would land, of course, would be anybody's guess but if found along some road or in a field, the curious discoverer would read instructions printed on its side to send it to the Weather Bureau. A special department of the Bureau devotes its entire time to reconditioning the radiosondes that are recovered and find their way home again.

By the time the men were ready to release the balloon a third man had arrived. He stayed inside the building, talking through an intercom to one of the men who was preparing the antenna in the big hemispheric shelter. He aimed the antenna in the general direction the balloon would go upon release, shouted "O.K.," and the men let go of the balloon. It started upward and the antenna moved, like the eye of a large mechanical cyclops, to follow its ascent. Motors whined and stopped, whined again as the machine made its own minute adjustments now on automatic tracking.

The man on the intercom called in to ask how the receiver and direction finder were functioning. The technician inside reported that the signals were being received and recorded. The other weatherman watched the radiosonde, now disappearing into the overcast. This had been a simple release, but he recalled others during the winter that were downright exciting. With a strong wind from the west or northwest the balloon would be swept horizontally at such a rate that the transmitter at the end of its long line was in danger of fouling on the telephone and power lines not more than a hundred yards away flanking the highway. Once it had fouled and the release had failed. At other times when snow drifted high in the lee of the hangar, the men had to scramble up the drifts, holding the transmitter until the balloon rose enough for the delicate instrument to clear the tops of larger drifts by the road which had been thrown up by the town's snowplows. It was, the watching weatherman concluded, interesting work at twenty below zero in a high wind, with snow driving so hard you couldn't see more than ten feet in front of you.

Both men returned to the station room. With the radiosonde out of sight in the clouds the only way to note its position was to watch the machines which were clicking and clacking at their designated tasks.

Now, for approximately a hundred minutes, the information would come in and, when it all had been recorded, would be interpreted and translated into the weather code for transmission to all other stations in the country.

At the time that the men at Caribou released the radiosonde, identical releases throughout the country occurred. More than sixty such instruments were now aloft, going higher and sending back the data that soon would form the next series of upper-atmosphere weather maps.

Inside the room, someone started coffee in the small urn on the table outside the washroom. One man made the hourly check of surface data and another began to interpret the teletypewriter messages and build the next surface weather map. When the coffee was ready the men solemnly matched nickels and the loser put payment for the three cups in a small box, the kitty from which coffee and occasionally doughnuts were purchased.

The night man finished his cup, said good-bye and made his weary way home.

To man the station at Caribou requires ten men working on three general shifts. A slight overlap at the beginning of one and end of another allows time for the men to discuss recent occurrences and pass on special information about equipment or phone calls that may come in.

Busiest of the three shifts is the first day watch. During this time the greatest work load is on the staff and inquiries from industry, anxious citizens, farmers and the Loring Air Force base—a Strategic Air Command outfit—are most likely to come in.

The meteorologist in charge, Walter Hattman, arrived at eight o'clock. His hours are technically those of an administrator but he works not only that time but also may drop in during the evening to catch up on reports or simply assure himself that everything is operating smoothly. Tall, crew-cut and methodical, he checked the maps on his arrival, read the general summary out of Washington, the early Boston forecast for the New England area and sat down to compose his own 8:30 forecast.

Millions of citizens have listened to their radio, at the breakfast table or while driving the car to work, and heard the station announcer saying, "And now we take you to the United States Weather Bureau office for the weather outlook today . . ." And most such citizens visualize switches being thrown, lights blinking on panels both in the radio station and the Weather Bureau room where the forecaster takes his cue from a buzzer or a light and begins to read into the microphone. At Caribou, the forecaster—in this case Mr. Hattman—sat at his desk listening to the small, battered table radio and the voice of the announcer as anyone else might do. And when *he* heard the announcer say, "And now we take you to the United States Weather Bureau . . ." he simply drew the microphone across the desk and after the announcer had finished, paused a few seconds and began reading his forecast. His own voice came out of the receiver at his elbow. It was the only way he could know whether he was on the air or not.

Essentially his forecast contained the local weather as the earlier relayed forecast had done. But it also included the information for New England and a summary of the weather over the rest of the country. From the shores of Washington and California, across the Rockies and the plains states down into the south and up along the Atlantic seaboard, the general conditions were spelled out.

At first thought, it may seem odd that people in Aroostook County would want to know the weather situation in, say California or Florida or South Dakota, but to the potato farmers and the shipping companies in Aroostook County this information is vital. Although Aroostook grows 15 per cent of all potatoes in the United States—the largest percentage in any single area—it has competition from growers in these other areas. Since the weather determines the quality and size of a crop, they want to keep track of the conditions during the growing season. It will determine the price they can get for their own crop and, for a shipper, will begin to tell him, as the season advances, how many trucks or freight cars he will need to meet the demand for shipments. Later in the season than August, when the Maine crop is harvested and stored, news of an early freeze in some other part of the country in fall or spring will put trucks on the road from Caribou going south to New York. Crops are sensitive goods and their prices reflect almost moment-by-moment changes in the weather throughout the country.

So vast and complex is the business of farming today that

new strains of potatoes, test-planted in Florida early in the season, may be rushed north to go into the Aroostook ground when it thaws and planting time comes to this largest of Maine's counties.

Many times the phone has rung in the small station at Caribou and the weatherman answering has found he was talking with a worried commodity broker in New York City. Yes, he knew what the general weather summary was for New England—and the country, too, for that matter. But what, precisely, was the weather now in Aroostook County? On it hinged prices and on those, of course, hinged the livelihood of the worried speculator. At other times, great buyers of potatoes —such as Gerber's Baby Foods—have called from Chicago inquiring about Aroostook weather and the outlook before and during the harvest. Would there be a good crop? What they really wanted to know, of course, was where could they buy potatoes cheapest in the United States. In Florida, South Dakota, California, Long Island or Aroostook County? The weatherman could give them a clue to the answer.

These occasional encounters with high finance, however, cannot divert a meteorologist long from his more basic occupation: eternally watching the sky with his own eyes, the eyes of radio and radar and every other means he can invent. It is the only way he can answer questions from far away, or those posed by the local chamber of commerce which wants a summary of climate conditions to advertise Caribou and Aroostook County and attract industry.

Northern Maine does have a surprisingly invigorating climate. Summers are cool and winters, though cold, are composed of dry cold air which makes low temperatures bearable. North of the rolling hills of Maine the Canadian wilderness stretches to the Arctic and from this region, during winter months, the polar air flows south to dominate the temperatures at such stations as Caribou.

The men in the Caribou station are accustomed to this seasonal change. Some are natives of the state and all, after one winter, have become veterans in the weather arena. Snowfalls that would paralyze such cities as Boston or New York are dealt with efficiently by hard-driving snowplow operators. When the large polar air masses come down bringing the snow, the first warning to everyone comes from the Caribou station. Within minutes of a snowfall's beginning, crews are on the road keeping ahead of the blowing snow, throwing it so high on the roadside that after several weeks of winter the huge bank diverts a new fall so that it sometimes blows entirely over the cleared road.

While the weathermen at the Caribou station are pleased by the road-clearing ability of the crews, they keep hoping someone will plow out around the hangar and the weather station. As each watch replaces the preceding one during heavy winter weather, the men park their cars on the road and clamber over seven- or ten-foot drifts to the half-buried station, the warm room and the eternally clacking teletypewriters. Some ski to work while the less athletic skywatchers sometimes snowshoe in to take their turn.

By midmorning of this August 22nd, the rain stopped. The low nimbostratus overcast had broken. The shreds of the clouds looked dark and untidy against the higher, lighter cloud cover. Occasionally a gleam of sunshine broke through and passed, like the beam of a searchlight, swiftly across the fields and hills and roads leading into the town.

In the weather station the men relaxed for a moment. The

upper-weather observation was complete, the data interpreted.
The receivers had been turned off. The side door opened and
a pilot came in. His plane, belonging to an industrial firm to
the south, sat on the ramp. The pilot had flown in to check on
contracts with the Loring Air Force base and, his work completed, hoped for good weather on his flight home.

Mr. Hattman briefed him, showed him the weather map and
let him read through the special advisories that were clipped
to a board near the door. As MIC, or meteorologist in charge,
Mr. Hattman had no authority to say whether the plane should
take off or not. All he could do was brief the pilot and give him
the outlook for various cities to the south over the next few
hours. The decision to fly, or not to fly, rested with the pilot
himself unless, of course, the field closed down.

In this case the pilot was experienced enough to understand
the weatherman's position. Many people, however, who call in
for weather information, expect to be told what to do. But
the weatherman who incautiously advises for or against an
undertaking on the basis of his forecast is overstepping
both his authority and the rules of common sense when dealing with a public that understands little of the weather problem.

Many a time weathermen have picked up the phone and
been confronted by a worried wife who asks, "Will it rain this
afternoon and if it does, for how long? What I mean is, is it
going to rain over near the river? You see, we planned a pic-
nic . . ." As calmly as possible, whoever answers the phone
repeats the latest forecast and may find his temperature rising
as the good taxpaying citizen persists and says, "Well, you're
supposed to know about the weather and if you can't tell me

whether it's going to rain over there before three o'clock, I don't see why I have to pay taxes for such . . ."

"Shall I have my daughter wear her rubbers to school this morning?"

"We were thinking of going to Bangor. Is it going to snow and if so, for how long, how much? Should we try to go?"

In the face of such inquiries most weathermen remain reasonably calm. But in the minds of many, some notable foolish question lingers and becomes a monument to ignorance of weather and the Weather Bureau's function. One such inquiry recalled by Mr. Hattman involved a farmer who called to ask how much rain would fall the next day in the Imperial Valley thousands of miles away in California.

Inevitably when the weatherman is wrong in his forecast people recollect that forecast almost verbatim to prove that they could do as well without half trying. Few people realize, however, that a change of a degree or two of temperature, a shift of wind of only a little bit, can bring rain or withhold it over a given area. The as yet unplumbed number of factors that go to make up the weather of a given place at a given moment is staggering. There well may be, in fact, some factors or combination of them whose importance meteorologists don't as yet suspect.

Forecasting is the riskiest part of a weatherman's work. He must not only know the condition of the atmosphere at the present but must also, by assuming certain things will happen, attempt to tell what the general and local weather are going to be. Naturally, as the extent of the forecast increases—either in time or geography—the less detailed it can be. Such a forecast takes present conditions and with the history of weather movements at particular seasons in particular areas combines to give a general prophecy. Temperatures above or below seasonal normals, precipitation more or less than average, and so on, give the best possible view ahead that man can yet obtain.

Between the periodic ringing of the phone, Caribou weathermen continue their ceaseless rounds of observations. Most of the data about the weather sweeping over this northern country are measured and recorded automatically. The changes in barometric pressure are traced on a barograph, the temperature on a thermograph. Wind speed and direction can be read at a glance from the dials in the room. Even the amount of solar radiation is automatically recorded for the benefit of the climatologist—and the chamber of commerce. But several instruments still require that Caribou weathermen go outside: the maximum-minimum thermometers, the precipitation gauge which measures the rainfall, and the psychrometer which measures humidity.

One measurement, presently only being made in two other locations in the United States, is the amount of ozone in the atmosphere. With a complex optical instrument, the amount is carefully noted thrice daily and transmitted to research men in Washington. The Caribou weathermen are not certain of its bearing on the weather or the use to which the research people in Washington put the information. But this rare form of oxygen—a three-atom molecule formerly thought to be formed only by electrical discharge through the atmosphere—may hold more information than appears at first glance. So the Caribou skywatchers have one more observation to record.

On his way home for lunch shortly after noon, Mr. Hattman drove through the center of Caribou, along Sweden Street and

21669

out to the western edge of town toward the country again. As he drove, he occasionally leaned forward and looked up through the windshield toward the sky.

The low, ragged, nimbus clouds were gone. An overcast of high cirrus clouds seemed about to break. The wind had shifted to a more westerly direction, gusty and cool. The road was still wet from the rain. On either side the soaked potato plants showed dark green, almost black in the fields. Nearly an inch of rain had fallen since early that morning.

When he returned to the station office the ceiling was high and broken enough to allow the men to take a visual sounding of the atmosphere. One man inflated a balloon identical to the one used earlier to determine the ceiling, a black sphere nearly four feet in diameter. Another man climbed an outside stairway at one corner of the hangar and slid back the protective cover on a small observatory hemisphere. He went into the enclosure and readied the theodolite. This instrument resembles a surveyor's transit but it also can read vertical angles. The observer snapped on an intercom connecting him to the recorder in the office. He made several rapid adjustments of the theodolite and then said "O.K." as he nodded to the man holding the balloon. It was released and, swaying slightly, rose above the hangar roof. Gusts of wind made the balloon move back and forth erratically as it rose at the pre-set rate of a thousand feet a minute. The observer squinted through the theodolite and picked it up, adjusting its image to the meeting point of two cross hairs. A warning buzzer sounded which gave him fifteen seconds to get set for a reading. When the signal came he glanced at the side of the theodolite and read the angles aloud. A voice acknowledging receipt of the data came to him over the intercom and the observer went back to tracking the balloon. Every minute, for as long as the balloon remained visible through the theodolite, he relayed the data to the man recording it in the station office.

With knowledge of the balloon's rate of ascent and the recorded angles, the wind speed and direction at upper levels of the atmosphere can be plotted. This method of obtaining upper-air soundings is less sophisticated than a radiosonde but it is cheaper, requires less equipment and can be carried out at all weather stations when the ceiling permits. Called a pibal observation—short for pilot balloon—it was the first truly successful method of sounding upper air developed by the Bureau and it is still in use.

While the pibal sounding was being taken, the man who had released the balloon was inside the station assembling data to produce a surface-weather map. In most stations surface maps are drawn every six hours. But Caribou, with its upper-air sounding responsibilities makes only two surface maps a day. The other two maps they produce are in the region of 18,000 to 20,000 feet where the pressure is 500 millibars or approximately half of the surface pressure.

As the afternoon passed, the hourly data began to fill the daily record sheet. The surface map, completed, took its place on top of the preceding maps. The clacking teletypewriters continued to spew forth information and Mr. Hattman or one of his colleagues occasionally tore the endless yellow sheet from the machine, snipped off a group of figures and placed them on the desk to be decoded and added to the station data.

Special advisories to pilots were clipped to a board near the side door through which the pilots usually entered.

From the National Meteorological Center near Washington came a thirty-hour prognostication. Many stations are equipped with facsimile receivers which allow direct reception of the periodic weather maps sent out by the Center showing the air mass weather over the entire northern hemisphere. Not so Caribou. They receive the information in code for the outlook over the northeast region. Mr. Hattman began plotting it as soon as it came off the wire. When he finished, he compared the Washington prognostication with his own surface map and frowned. Washington foresaw a small front developing and moving toward Caribou that could bring rain. His own map didn't indicate that would occur. Who was right?

At six, with his forecast prepared, he waited to go on the air and give the evening weather report and forecast. When he heard the station introduce him ". . . and we take you now to the U.S. Weather Bureau station in Caribou," he pulled the microphone in place and began.

"Cloudy with a few lingering showers passing through the area tonight. Low tonight 45 to 50. Partly cloudy and warmer Wednesday. High 70 to 75. Fair and not much change in temperature Wednesday night. Low Wednesday night 48 to 52. Northwesterly winds 10 to 15 miles per hour this evening, becoming light and variable later tonight, and westerly 10 to 20 miles per hour Wednesday. . . . During the past twenty-four hours we have had nearly an inch of rainfall in Caribou. In Houlton the rainfall was . . ."

But as he read the statistics of the past weather his mind was on the difference between his weather map and the outlook sent from Washington. Maybe they saw something he didn't. His present map, of course, couldn't tell him exactly what would occur a day and a half ahead—not even when compared with the preceding maps. All it could do was point toward the possibilities. The Center, with maps of many layers of the atmosphere, with all that data at their fingertips was in a better position. But the question remained: Would the weak frontal system form and bring a spate of rain, or not?

The truck drivers who had sat in the Victory Restaurant early that morning were now far to the south, driving fast toward the city markets.

The waitresses were off duty and neither thought about the weather except to express relief that the rain had stopped, "Thank goodness!"

The farmers, coming into their homes through the kitchen door, were too tired to worry about the weather.

The sun lowered behind a new bank of clouds to the west. Lights came on in the farmhouses. In the weather station the phone rang. Mr. Hattman picked it up absently. His wife wanted to know when he would be home for supper. Mr. Hattman put on his jacket and stepped outside. As he walked toward his car he looked up, taking another, but by no means final, look at the sky.

CHAPTER 2

Station Idlewild

EACH YEAR, day by day, more than eight million air travelers stream through the nation's largest air terminal: New York International Airport. More than a million of these arrive from abroad—from Buenos Aires, London, Rome, New Delhi and many other places. In steadily increasing numbers, the people of the world casually step aboard a high-flying jet air transport which rises swiftly into the great ocean of air which is under the constant surveillance of the skywatchers.

New York International Airport, or Idlewild as it is known, is one of the world's busiest, most complex airports. It is the arrival point for nearly 75 per cent of all incoming travelers to the United States. Where tourists to the United States used to look for the Statue of Liberty to symbolize the end of their trip, they now search the low, flat eastern shore of Long Island as the plane loses altitude for a sight of the shining new buildings and long runways that is Idlewild. Forty airlines operate from Idlewild—of which twenty-three are foreign owned. Each normal day of operation sees an average of 640 landings and take-offs—or one every 2¼ minutes around the clock all year long.

Thanks largely to advances in meteorology most days at Idlewild are "normal" for flight operations.

On one such normal day in November, rain came from
clouds that hung 500 feet above the glistening runways. As at
Caribou, the rain began during the early hours of the morning
but as the day advanced it increased in intensity and the black
clouds lowered until they seemed to scrape the eleven-story
flight-control tower. Not far away in Manhattan the upper parts
of the tall buildings did penetrate the cloud base. On the ex-
pressways leading to and from the city the rain formed rivers
that jammed the drainage system and made driving hazardous.
It was so dark at Idlewild that even at midmorning lights blazed
in all the buildings.

The rain was not gentle. It came down in torrents. Wind
sent showers of it swirling and dancing across the roads and
the runways and the sidewalks. In the briefing room in the
Arrival Building a BOAC pilot talked with the weatherman
on duty. A bank of teletypewriters clacked noisily along one
wall—linking the station to Caribou, Washington and all the
other weather stations. At one end of the room a television
screen displayed a series of weather maps. The voice of a forecaster, taped in another part of the station on the opposite side
of the field, came into the room. Maps of surface weather,
upper-air and distant weather appeared briefly and then dis-
appeared from the screen. At the end of seven minutes, the
last map vanished. Soon a slightly revised set of maps began its
slow journey across the screen. The BOAC pilot studied the
TV screen carefully. He was a smallish, sophisticated-looking
man, wearing shiny black shoes, a neat flight uniform with a
row of service ribbons above his left pocket. His flight cap was

set at a jaunty angle. The pilot's flight was New York to Bermuda. He turned from the TV screen and began to ask the weatherman questions. The skywatcher walked from one teletypewriter to another, eying the information there, pointing out items to the flight captain. The skywatcher was in his shirtsleeves. He wore glasses and looked tired. He made his remarks calmly and with detachment. The pilot listened intently, not missing a word.

A flurry of wind sent a curtain of water rattling against the window. The flight captain glanced at it. Over that sound came the whine of jet engines winding up to full power, screaming over the wind. On the runway a grayish-silver plane, partially obscured by the rain, gathered speed, lifted off and nosed sharply upward to disappear almost instantly in the opaque, black clouds.

The British pilot turned from the window and peered closely at the facsimile of an upper-weather map that had come in from Washington. On it the weather-briefing meteorologist traced the expected course of the system that was at that moment drenching the roads and runways and buildings. The flight captain asked several more questions which were agreeably answered. The flier didn't appear nervous but he grasped all the information he could. When he was satisfied, he thanked the weatherman, smiled and left. Fully assured, he would go to his plane and, when cleared by the control tower, would take the plane off, going immediately on instruments as he climbed into the cloud cover. In his mind would be, among other things, a picture of the weather map he had been studying in the skywatcher's office.

The weatherman walked over and turned down the volume

on the television briefing screen so that the pictures came and went silently.

Two miles across the field in the forecast section where the TV camera was transmitting the briefing on a closed circuit, the aluminum sheets to which the maps were fastened fell one on top of the other at pre-set intervals and the only sound they made was a slight "whoosh" as air cushioned their fall. Outside the small alcove where the tape machine and map display case were located, men worked bent over a long table. Pinned on racks before them were sheaves of facsimile maps. One man picked up a bundle of maps on which he'd been working and went to fasten them to the aluminum sheets, readying them for TV display. Another man spoke into a microphone, taping a revised forecast. When he finished he put the tape in the machine and started it. Farther down the long room another table was covered with blank outline maps with station marks dotting the surface. Young men, reading weather code from yellow sheets torn from the omnipresent teletypewriters, worked swiftly filling the station circles with data. When a map was filled with the data, it went to the drawing table where more experienced men began sketching the isobars swiftly, their hands moving in long sweeps as they drew the lines, first in pencil and then in different colored inks.

Mr. Silvio Simplicio, the supervising forecaster, concentrated on a small map of the tropopause—that division of the troposphere and stratosphere. He sketched in the lines of equal pressure with pencil and then, after several erasures and shifting of lines, drew the final ones in purple.

Mr. Simplicio, a graduate meteorologist who had received his training at New York University (see p. 149) is a slight man of medium height. His wiry black hair is touched with gray and he moves about his work with a quick step. He is rarely still. Either he peers over the shoulder of one of his colleagues or busies himself drawing maps, his hands moving swiftly, surely over the charts. As he draws, he concentrates all his attention on the job at hand. Almost automatically he interprets the data in the station circles and interpolates between stations, placing the lines in smooth curves where they should go. When he finishes, he takes the map to a light table and begins to ink in the lines, readying it for radio facsimile transmission to other stations. When the map is completed the lines look as though they had been drawn by machine. But there is no machine yet that can do the job as well as forecasters like Mr. Simplicio.

In the troubled boundaries between great air masses, where much of the weather we experience occurs, there still are too many unknown factors to be able to formularize them and feed them to a computer which in turn could activate a map-drawing machine. There is such a machine in Washington but it is only useful in projecting the air-mass situation on paper. It does this job well and swiftly. But along frontal systems, in occlusions, like the one hanging over Idlewild, the machine cannot operate. Experience like that of Mr. Simplicio is required and it cannot yet be fed to a computer. As he draws and works, Mr. Simplicio himself is probably not aware of every bit of information that is being brought to bear on the control of his pen. A forecaster working in a local area for a number of years has a file system in his unconscious. Many weather maps of the past are, figuratively, stored there. Weather situations tend to repeat themselves and if a forecaster sees a familiar one looming on the map he is drawing, its relation to one he has seen years ago will help guide his hand: *In that similar situation, in that area, for reasons perhaps unknown, the frontal path goes like this*—and the hand holding the pen moves swiftly on without pausing. Or the forecaster may be simultaneouly assessing several maps of situations widely spaced in time, yet each having some characteristic similar to the present one. *This motion of cold air will overcome this northward-moving warm moist air if the pressure gradient . . . The result will be northeasterly movement, bringing an end to the precipitation . . .* And so he builds yet another forecast.

No. No machine can yet do Mr. Simplicio's job nor that of the twenty other forecasters who plot maps and prepare forecasts around the clock in the busiest airport in the world.

The public sees little of the Idlewild group of skywatchers. In the New York area the weather station in the glamorous RCA buildings handles the crowds of school children and tourists while doing its own job of skywatching. Atop the RCA building stands a sensitive radar set that scans the weather for a radius of more than 250 miles around the city. It sees rain in Pennsylvania, snow in western Massachusetts and fog in Connecticut. Endlessly scanning the skies around this great metropolitan complex, it sends a picture of what it sees to screens where men like Mr. Simplicio can read directly the goings on of the atmosphere and report it with confidence.

As in the small station at Caribou, Maine, the skywatchers at Idlewild send up radiosondes twice a day. With the information received, maps are drawn for the upper atmosphere at various pressure levels all the way to the lower edge of the stratosphere. Jet flights, flying west to San Francisco and Los

Angeles and beyond, or eastward to Europe, Africa and Asia rise to heights of 40,000 feet. From his pressurized cabin the passenger gets little impression of such height, for beyond a certain level—and until the fringes of space are reached—the eye makes little distinction between the earth seen from 20,000 feet and the same patch of real estate seen at 40,000 feet. Many times the passenger sees only the white or gray undercast of clouds far below him. Above the plane the sun shines brilliantly in a clear sky. The air is smooth. It is in this region of the atmosphere that upper-air soundings are most valuable for aviation purposes. On the maps drawn by the forecasters at Idlewild in the 300 millibar or 150 millibar region the much-dramatized jet streams appear for the first time. These high rivers of air with their strong currents can help or hinder a jet flight tremendously. Since they move from west to east in the northern hemisphere, westbound planes like to avoid them; eastbound planes are sometimes assisted by the air rivers. But unlike popular conceptions of the jet streams, the actual belts of air currents are not regular and not always continuous. They may appear as winding, interrupted paths on the maps.

As higher and higher maps are drawn of a weather situation, anyone who studies them can see that by leaving the surface weather far below, the entire picture shown by isobars is simplified. Mountains, deserts, oceans and large lakes do not exert their turbulent effect on the upper reaches of air. Oceans, of course, play a major role in weather formation but primarily, at these altitudes, as a contributor of moisture and a temperature modifier. Squall lines, thunderheaded cumulus, most disturbing weather features disappear save for a few giant storm centers that may reach, in some cases, as high as 60,000 feet.

Air travelers up in the jet highways are indeed flying over the weather—over the weather they knew below but not over the winds. Of major importance to pilots at those altitudes are the winds. Jet stream winds, of course, sometimes reach levels of 200 or 300 knots. But even outside these great air movements, winds are a factor. If a westbound pilot flies at an airspeed of 600 knots and is faced with a 200-knot headwind it will cut his ground speed to two thirds of his indicated air speed—and that can affect his arrival time and his maximum safe-flying range with a given amount of fuel. So Mr. Simplicio and his colleagues draw the winds as well as the isobars for these maps. Lines of equal wind speed are known as isotachs and they appear on the upper-air maps, though in a different color ink.

At one end of the room in Hangar 11 at Idlewild, where the forecasters work, are three radio facsimile map transmitters and three receivers. As the approved, final maps continue to come from the big table, they are sent by facsimile to the regions affected. On the floor above, the Federal Aviation Authority takes periodic reports from the forecast section and places them on the correct teletypewriter circuit. Some are radio teletypewriters. Of immediate and primary concern to all Idlewild personnel is the weather between New York and London. So great is the air traffic between Idlewild and London that a "private line" links the two stations. Other "party line" machines link other main distribution points—Miami to the south where appropriate reports fan out to cover the northern coast of the South American continent and the Caribbean area; the Azores to the east which sends information along to Europe and to Mediterranean and African stations; Montreal which feeds Canada and the Arctic weather stations. This vast overseas net both sends and receives reports so that Idlewild becomes the major link between the east coast of the United States and the world to the north, south and east of it. The regular nationwide teletype network functions to the west and Idlewild is a part of that, too. Reports stream in not only from Detroit and Minneapolis and Denver and San Francisco but also from more distant points such as Alaska, Hawaii, Japan and the South Pacific areas.

There is no time in this busy center for individual research projects. The press of business—both of weather reporting and forecasting and of pilot briefing—keeps everyone busy through each man's eight-hour tour of duty. Coffee breaks and leisurely chats among skywatchers at Caribou have no counterpart here. For the weather which changes with every hour and every minute without end has become, for the skywatchers, the master not the servant of their interest. They must observe it without interruption. They must keep their eyes fixed on it, on the data and the instruments that tell them what it is. They cannot miss any aspect of it. For every $2\frac{1}{4}$ minutes another flight is arriving, another leaving.

It is this continual arriving and departing that makes knowledge of the local weather surrounding New York City so critically important. Although the radar set atop the RCA building can help, it cannot tell the meteorologist all he must know. Today at an airport like Idlewild, he must know from second to second what the ceiling is, what the visibility is, for the pilot must be safely cleared for take-off and informed for his landing. The crude Pibal method of determining the ceiling at Caribou will not do here. Men cannot run out and inflate balloons every thirty seconds and then merely estimate with a stopwatch what the height of the cloud base is. They must know all the time and accurately.

To determine this important measurement, a special instrument called a rotating-beam ceilometer has been developed. Using infrared radiation, a beam is played on the base of the cloud and the spot where it strikes is picked up by a sensitive receiver. A machine automatically calculates the height of the cloud above ground. As the beam of the ceilometer rotates, the ceiling over the entire airfield—which covers 4900 acres—is automatically defined and reported.

Augmenting the valuable work of the ceilometer is another device called a transmissometer which reports on changing visibility on the instrument runway which planes use when the ceiling is very low. With these two instruments operating, the control tower can relay the information to incoming pilots, telling them exactly when they will break out of the cloud cover and where they should be able to spot the instrument runway lights.

Such instrumentation that measures and reports continually on very local weather near busy airfields the size of Idlewild has resulted in more continuous flying—some of it under conditions which a few years ago would have canceled all outgoing and incoming flights. Today, for example, with the help of these instruments, a pilot may be cleared for take-off when the ceiling is as low as 150 feet.

Another instrument under test will help solve another problem facing all skywatchers. It is a cloud-cover indicator. During the day, the best an observer can do to determine cloud cover is go out and look. Even then, if low clouds are covering most of the sky, he cannot tell what clouds in what amounts exist above the ones that block his vision. But the instrument now under test will do it by scanning the sky in a spiral pattern, focusing first on low clouds, then searching out the higher ones and scanning those with the help of special radar. In the past any attempt to report the extent of cloud cover of even the lowest level was pretty much a hit-or-miss affair. With the new indicator a round-the-clock accuracy far surpassing anything known before will be possible.

The impact that flying has had on the Weather Bureau since about 1940 is nearly incalculable. Today, aside from the regular job of observing and reporting daily weather, the largest service the skywatchers render is in providing weather information to fliers. World War II, of course, demanded a great number of meteorologists—more than the Bureau had or could supply without weakening the weather network so painstakingly built during the pre-war years. To fill the needs of wartime flying—when flying truly became a global operation—the Navy and Army had to train many of their own meteorologists to man the growing number of stations.

The impact of this training is still evident. Many men today employed by the Bureau in its post-war expansion were trained by the military services during the war. By 1945 the Air Corps had regularly scheduled flights literally around the world. From England to the Azores to Gander, Newfoundland, to Westover Field, Massachusetts—to Hamilton Field, California, to Hawaii, to Guam, the Philippines and Australia, to India and the Middle East and back to England. Weather, too, had to become global but the number of stations was not large enough to do all that had to be done. In combat areas many planes were lost because of adverse unreported weather and

many transport planes went down on routes over which little
or no weather data could be gathered. Once the war ended,
the boom in commercial aviation began. It has yet to end. With
the advent of jet transports a new era in aviation began—and
of weather study, too.

Before each take-off of even the smallest plane for only a
short flight between airports, the pilot should check the weather.
So that he can, the Weather Bureau maintains first order observation stations such as that at Caribou and at Idlewild which
are designated as Weather Bureau Airport Stations. Although
the traffic at Caribou is light and made up almost entirely of
small planes on relatively short cross-country hops, it supplies
any pilot with the necessary weather information while at the
same time continuing its endless surveillance of the weather
and the reporting at regular intervals of the necessary information by teletypewriter to every other station on the network.
Today there are about 240 Weather Bureau Airport Stations
ranging in size from giant Idlewild to small Caribou. But this
has not proved to be enough. To meet the growing demand for
weather briefing the Bureau recently set up a training program
at the Federal Aviation Agency school in Oklahoma City.

The FAA, as it is abbreviated, is the renamed Civil Aeronautics Authority and has the responsibility for issuing all
flight-control instructions and handling communications between hundreds of airports in the United States and other
countries. Many FAA personnel help man the control towers
where instruction to incoming and outgoing planes originate.
No plane in such an airport may as much as taxi from its
parking spot without clearance from the tower. Incoming
planes are cleared to land or told to fit into a holding flight

pattern at specified altitudes until runways are open. The FAA, in short, supplies the discipline and control for safe flying. It is a large responsibility and weather briefing plays a big part in making safe decisions and giving intelligent instructions and advice to pilots.

Thus the two organizations—the Weather Bureau and the Federal Aviation Agency—find their interests and needs overlapping. Through cooperative effort the Bureau ran the five-month course at Oklahoma City during 1961. As a result, the Bureau now has trained the first group of 4000 Flight Service Specialists of the FAA in pilot weather briefing. On some fields there are no bureau stations and hence no firsthand briefing by Bureau men is possible. With the training, however, many FAA men will be qualified to brief pilots on the latest weather conditions to be met in their flight paths.

At the outset of the course the Bureau announced, with pardonable satisfaction, that by the end of the first year an additional 330 FAA Flight Service stations and eighty FAA combined station towers would have personnel who could brief pilots. Under this expanded program the trained FAA men will adapt Weather Bureau information to meet each pilot's flight needs. If problems arise that the briefing man cannot handle for lack of reference to latest maps and advisories, they can be solved quickly and easily as all the new briefing posts are linked with the nearest Weather Bureau station by private telephone or teletypewriter. To supplement the course of training at Oklahoma City, the Bureau has developed texts and aids to allow FAA men to qualify by their own study and by passing an examination made up by experienced meteorologists of the Bureau.

The responsibility for advising pilots falls on the forecaster on duty at such small stations as Caribou. At Idlewild, distinct separation of duties within the group of meteorologists allows the usual work of map preparation and forecasting to proceed without interruption. Routine weather observations, analysis and reports are in themselves compartmented to a large extent. Although the radiosondes originate atop the building in which the forecasting and map section works, the men tending the receivers, the direction-finding antenna, the balloon release—all those aspects of the job—might as well be miles away so far as Mr. Simplicio and his colleagues are concerned. To them comes only the data: weather in capsuled symbolized form for them to work with. Hourly reports of wind speed, direction, cloud cover and all the related information for surface reports is taken two miles from the forecasting section across the busy air terminal in the Arrival Building where the briefing office is located.

The forecasters and map makers are, in fact, so removed from data taking that they have only one instrument in the office: a barograph which continuously records the rise and fall of surface pressure. Even this is not essential for the forecaster's operation. But perhaps the men put it there merely to reassure themselves that the weather is not all symbols and paper and code and black and purple and orange lines on a map.

That the weather was and is a palpable thing was never more evident than on that rainy day in November. The surface map, which one of the meteorologists was preparing, showed a shaded green precipitation area on both sides of a slightly curving line which ended almost over Idlewild. The line was dotted, alternately, with semi-circles and arrowheads indicating the location of an occluded front. From the north and west a mass of cold, dry air was sweeping in a counterclockwise motion chasing a mass of warm, moist air and pushing it upward. As the moist air rose, the water vapor condensed and fell as the torrents of rain that were striking the windows. The occluded front moved slowly as the morning progressed. The rain was continuous. It filled the low places of the parking lot outside and the mailman and other visitors to the building that morning entered with water squirting from their shoes, their trouser cuffs drenched.

Under the fluorescent lights at the map table the men drew and consulted and fiddled with pencils, forming the words of a forecast. Anyone watching them would have thought that weather over their heads and outside their window was the farthest thing from their minds. One of the men passed by the barograph and glanced at it.

"There it goes." He almost shouted and hurried to the window. Others dropped their pens and pencils and joined him. Three or four crowded around the window and peered up into the gray clouds.

The marking pen on the barograph had been showing lower and lower pressure on the graph as the occluded front approached. The invisible line in the sky, marking the front and placed with so much confidence on the surface map, moved at the predicted rate. When it passed over the building, the barograph pen moved vertically upward, showing an immediate rise in pressure. The warm side of the front had gone and the cold, heavier air was now above the men.

They watched the flag on the mast outside the window. It

would have to do in place of a wind-direction instrument. As the front moved by, the wind direction changed nearly 180 degrees and moved with increasing speed, gusty, sending the rain swirling across the parking lot in a direction opposite that of a moment before. The front passed on time, on schedule and with all the expected characteristics.

Skywatchers who had spent fourteen years forecasting at Idlewild, men at the top of their difficult and challenging profession, still had not lost the sense of delight that comes from predicting, on the nose, another of the atmosphere's endless occurrences. One of the men at the window turned away finally, glanced at the barograph and returned to the current surface map. The lines and the green-shaded area and the abbreviated data by the station symbol that was Idlewild became for him at the moment not just a chore of data processing, but man's best effort to reduce the flowing atmosphere to order and to meaning. They had done it. And in his mind he formed the forecast to come: "Wind decreasing and moving to a westerly direction. Colder tonight with rain ending by midafternoon. . . ."

Mr. Simplicio put the finishing touches on his portrait of the tropopause. He had heard the rush to the window but his only reaction had been a brief turning of his head to watch the men. A smile touched his face. They never got over the excitement of it. It was a good thing they didn't.

CHAPTER 3

Station Washington

THE MAN ultimately responsible for the activities at such stations as Caribou and Idlewild is the Presidentially appointed Chief of the U.S. Weather Bureau. The man who held that post longest, Dr. F. W. Reichelderfer, served from 1938 to 1963 and guided the Bureau during its greatest period of growth. As is often the case, the times produce the man. Dr. Reichelderfer was literally born during the era of the Bureau's initial expansion and modernization. He grew up with aviation which today employs so much of the Bureau's time and effort.

In 1918, as a young officer in the Navy, he underwent flight training in Miami and Pensacola, Florida. In 1919 he went to Lisbon, Portugal, and sent back weather information for the Navy's aircraft which made the first aerial transatlantic crossing. During the 1920's he took part in free balloon races, getting a taste of upper-atmosphere sounding. Still in the Navy, he received further weather training during a tour aboard the dirigible U.S.S. *Los Angeles*. Later he served as a U.S. Navy observer aboard the ill-fated *Hindenburg*. He organized new meteorological services for the Navy and developed training and forecasting methods. Consequently, when he took charge of the Bureau in 1938, he was well prepared to face the explosion of meteorological activity brought on by the outbreak of World War II.

By the time the United States entered the war, even the most tradition-bound infantry commander realized that control of the air was essential to military success. The aerial activities of the British, Japanese and Germans left little room for doubt. But to send aircraft on military missions required a knowledge of weather. To the relatively new Chief of Bureau the question "weather where?" was easily answered. Weather over the whole northern hemisphere.

Until this time the activities of the Bureau had been largely confined to the United States. Such adjacent areas as the Caribbean had been covered but the Bureau lacked funds to extend its network to Alaska, Hawaii and beyond or to the shores of Greenland and the Arctic seas.

World War II changed all that overnight. On December 26, 1941, less than three weeks after the Japanese attacked Pearl Harbor, Dr. Reichelderfer received an executive order permitting him to coordinate all U.S. civilian meteorological services, all special projects related to transoceanic flights and all international meteorological meetings and missions to other countries. In this emergency the groundwork of the present unique nerve center of U.S. meteorological work was created.

By February of 1942, Dr. Reichelderfer had in operation the new Analysis Center in Washington, D.C. Its purposes were to bring the fundamental activities—data assessment and forecasting—under one roof and so eliminate conflicting national and international forecasts, and to aid local forecasters in their assessment of daily weather.

In those crucial days weather over the North Atlantic between the United States and Europe became of utmost importance for the supply of beleagured England. Weather over the South Atlantic assumed almost equal importance since the air route to the embattled African front lay across that ocean. Our own predicament in the Pacific demanded quick action. The weather over those thousands of watery miles became increasingly important. The Philippines were invaded. Supplies and arms sent by ship cost too much precious time. Air supply had to become a reality overnight. In addition, military planes had to get to island and Australian bases as fast as possible.

Today, with the huge efficient network operating smoothly, it is nearly impossible to relive those tense and fearful days. But it is plain to even the most casual observer that weather had become in one instant a big business. Big business in a military sense then; big business now in both a commercial and military sense.

From the time the Analysis Center was established in those war days of 1942 it has continued to operate, a large, tireless machine, twenty-four hours a day, 365 days a year. In 1958 the Analysis Center became part of the newly organized National Meteorological Center and moved to new headquarters in Suitland, Maryland, just outside Washington. The administrative headquarters of the Bureau remained in a modernized and expanded building at the corner of 24th and M streets in the center of the nation's capital.

The new National Meteorological Center is composed of four branches. At the core of the organization lies the Analysis and Forecast Branch. The three other components are the

Extended Forecast Branch, the Development Branch, and the Computation Branch.

Each branch plays its part in the work of getting data from the farthest reaches of the northern hemisphere, processing it, analysing it and creating forecasts, all *within a time span of three hours.*

The size of the job done by the National Meteorological Center can be understood quickly by viewing the amount of material it receives. Every twenty-four hours, NMC receives:

25,500 hourly surface reports
11,700 international six-hourly surface reports
3200 ship reports
900 pibal winds aloft reports
980 radiosonde reports
500 rawinsonde reports
1000 reports from commercial aircraft in flight
400 scheduled military air weather reconnaissance reports
100 encoded transmissions
54 facsmile transmissions.

This is the raw material. It flows in, an unending stream that must be digested quickly, efficiently and tirelessly. It must be reduced, packaged, drawn, graphed, encoded and sent out.

The Analysis and Forecast Branch

The data the Analysis and Forecast Branch receives—more than 30,000 separate reports each twenty-four hours—arrives at the Communications Section on twenty teletypewriters or by wire or radio from all over the world.

After reception, it is taken to the plotting room where more than twenty men and women per shift work on large map sections of the northern hemisphere. Each is filled with the data and, then, like pieces of a huge jigsaw puzzle they are fitted together. Sometimes a section is completed by one man while other larger sections are handled by groups of plotters. When the maps, whether surface or upper air, are covered with the code notations of all the weather measurements, they are ready for analysis. The maps are spread out on huge light tables where teams of men draw the forms of the isobars, interpreting the plotted data. As they draw, the great air masses of the northern hemisphere begin to take shape on a piece of paper.

When the analysis is finished, the completed maps go to the Prognostic room. Here, experts prepare prognostic charts, foretelling the weather. These "progs," as they are called, are taken to the Communications room and sent out either by facsimile radio or encoded teletype message to more than seven hundred users of the information: Bureau stations, Air Force and Naval installations and FAA stations. Concise and on time these prognostic charts arrive at Mr. Hattman's station in Caribou, Maine, and in Mr. Simplicio's office at Idlewild Airport.

Each day of the year the Analysis and Forecast Branch produces hundreds of maps for transmission. Among them are maps of present weather in the United States on the surface and at various altitudes up to 60,000 feet, a surface map of hemisphere weather, prognostic charts that look eighteen and thirty hours ahead of anticipated cloud conditions, twenty-four-hour temperature change forecasts and expected amounts of rainfall for all regions of the United States.

In addition to this mammoth job, the Analysis and Forecast Branch acts as a consultant to and coordinator for all Bureau stations, Navy and Air Force weathermen who are involved with developing storm centers.

It also trains meteorologists for special assignments and is the one Bureau installation capable of carrying out special projects concerned with weather around the globe.

Extended Forecast Branch

The Extended Forecast Branch of the National Meteorological Center concerns itself primarily with the weather beyond the normal twenty-four-hour or thirty-six-hour daily forecasts broadcast to the public with every weather report. For years skywatchers have dreamed of predicting weather accurately over long periods of time. The benefit to agriculture is obvious. To be able to forewarn of a severe winter, excessive or minimum precipitation, or unusually hot summers would govern farmers' planning for the months ahead. Not so obvious, although equally important, is the benefit to industry. Manufactures' shipping schedules, anticipated loads on power supply facilities, and fuel distributors' plans all are affected by weather. If they can know what it will be far enough in advance, they can operate more efficiently and save hundreds of thousands of dollars each year.

As its history shows, the Weather Bureau often has had to wait for a crisis to get funds with which to realize the dreams of skywatchers. The Extended Forecast Branch grew out of a crisis: the 1935 dust bowl calamity. In that fateful year bad farming practices of past years, coupled with unrelieved drought, turned much of our Midwest farmland into desert. Thousands of families abandoned their desolated homes and headed toward California, the promised land, in one of the largest migrations in American history. Behind them they left toppled windmills, dry wells, barren fields from which all the topsoil had been stripped by the dry winds. Here and there a few corn stalks, bent and crushed by the shifting dunes of subsoil jutted from the deserted earth.

It is doubtful that even if the skywatchers had known the drought years were coming, they would have been able to prevent them. Irrigation projects require many years to complete. Reeducation of farmers requires as many more. But the catastrophe did focus attention on the problem of long-range forecasting.

Congress quickly allocated funds under the Bankhead-Jones Act to begin research on extended forecasting. The Weather Bureau, the Bureau of Agricultural Economics and the Department of Meteorology of the Massachusetts Institute of Technology pooled resources to begin the project.

All schemes and theories purporting to foretell weather far ahead of its arrival were analyzed. The soundest aspects of all theories were taken and eventually combined into an experimental method of operating such a forecast group. When the scheme had been worked out and tested, it was moved to Washington, six years after the initial attack on the problem.

Soon another factor entered the picture. As war approached, the military services showed great interest in long-range forecasting. They wanted to know general weather conditions in certain areas months ahead of time. They also wanted to know short-term—one- or two-week—weather along shipping routes. As in many military situations since history began (see p. 110) the supply and use of fighting groups depends in many cases on weather. When war requirements overshadowed basic research in the field of long-range forecasting, the Extended Forecast Section was already working to understand the global nature of weather.

The method developed in these prewar years is now, with many extensions and refinements, the basis for the five- and thirty-day forecasts made by this group. Here in a very simplified way, is how it works. When all available data is assembled, local influences are removed from the mass of material and the remaining data analyzed. Great deviations from the normal pattern of weather for the season are noted and by predicting the effects of such deviations, the Extended Forecast Section issues its results.

Today this gigantic task is done by using computers and elaborate physical and statistical methods. The essential premise underlying these forecasts is this: The atmosphere attempts to reach a level or state of equilibrium. This it would do if nothing disturbed or prevented it. But solar energy, abnormal seasonal temperatures and other factors do not permit the atmosphere to "come to rest" so to speak. Nevertheless, the fluid air is always trying to do this. By noting the size and direction of the disturbing effects and knowing how the atmosphere will attempt to return to an equilibrium state, these farsighted skywatchers can, with increasing success, tell what the weather characteristics will be for periods a number of days ahead.

As their knowledge grows, as their techniques are refined and as meaningless data is weeded out, the percentage of accurate forecasts will rise. Today the percentage is higher than in previous years in nearly all areas of forecasting. Forecasting of precipitation appears to be the most difficult aspect.

Five-day forecasts are made for periods beginning two days after the forecast is made, which in effect makes it a seven-day prognostication. These are issued to field offices each Sunday, Tuesday and Thursday. The overlapping of the forecast periods allows revision to be made every two days. These forecasts form the basis for the familiar TV and radio reports to the public which give anticipated weather for several days in advance. They include a prediction of average hemispheric circulation at sea level and at approximately 10,000 feet. This average is then broken down and forms the daily pressure charts which locate fronts, air masses and precipitation areas for each of the five days. Also included are the expected abnormality of temperatures and the precipitation totals anticipated within the contiguous United States.

Twice monthly the Extended Forecast Branch issues a thirty-day outlook. Again the overlap allows some revision in the light of later data. The thirty-day forecast includes patterns of air currents above the earth's surface, prevailing tracks of cyclones and anticyclonic areas, anticipated abnormal temperatures and precipitation patterns.

This longer-range outlook is, of course, subject to greater error than the short-range forecasts. The thirty-day forecast is published in a bulletin titled "The Average Monthly Weather Résumé and Outlook." It not only includes the forecast period but also the weather pattern that actually occurred during the preceding thirty-day period.

So far as the public is presently concerned, the five- and thirty-day forecasts are the only visible activities of this branch of the NMC. Much, however, is going on behind the scenes. Extended Forecast is trying to look even farther into the future. One of their present research efforts is directed at attempts to relate the long-range patterns of air circulation to the prediction of seasonal weather over the hemisphere. What this means is that eventually the skywatchers hope to be able with reasonable accuracy to foretell the seasons. Will winter be exceptionally cold in any given area? Will there be abnormal snowfall? Will spring bring floods? Will the summer bring drought? For the past few years, the Extended Forecast Branch has been preparing seasonal outlooks four times a year—but not yet for public distribution. The outlooks are part of the research. Only when the key factors controlling seasonal weather are found and measured will predictions be made public.

Many other research projects fill the Branch's time. Among them are: Studies of atmospheric energy sources; studies of the effects of the earth's surface on circulation; statistical studies relating temperatures, rainfall and pressure of one season to another; studies relating the origin and paths of hurricanes to general air circulation; continuing studies to increase the accuracy of both short- and long-range forecast techniques.

Actually, the Extended Forecast Branch is a huge laboratory combining day-to-day operations with basic research. Meteorologists from field stations come to it on temporary assignments to complete various research projects and to look into the future of their profession. The Branch's entire facility is available to visiting meteorologists and atmospheric physicists; frequently, foreign observers come to view the Bureau's effort and to study its modern practices. All its data on hemispheric circulation and the dynamics of the atmosphere are available to both foreign and domestic groups whether private or governmental.

Numerical Weather Prediction Branch

Another component of the National Meteorological Center is the Numerical Weather Prediction Branch. It represents the most advanced scheme of forecasting yet devised by men. In cooperation with Navy and Air Force meteorologists, Bureau skywatchers have attained completely automatic data analysis and weather prediction.

Field office routines such as the small one at Caribou and the larger, more impressive one at Idlewild shrink to the point of invisibility when compared to the concepts being worked out by NWP meteorologists.

From its beginning, NWP turned toward modern computers. The earliest computer employed was capable of doing computations that would have been impossible for humans to complete on time. For example, in one second the now outdated computer could add a column of figures as high as the Washington monument. The newest computer is between six and ten times as fast, depending upon the operation being performed. Since any weather measurements are quickly succeeded by new observations, the speed with which they can be processed and drawn on maps is of primary importance.

Twice a day data from observation stations all over the hemisphere come to NWP Branch by teletypewriters and are recorded directly on magnetic tape. A computer reads the information from the magnetic tape, sorting the information, locating it geographically, and then directing yet another machine to draw the weather map automatically.

In this latest system using advanced machines all human intervention is eliminated. The machines take the material from the teletypewriters, assess it and produce the weather map of the hemisphere. The importance of the NWP operation can be sensed when it is realized that the Strategic Air Command of the United States Air Force must know the weather over Texas and the weather which will exist over Greenland at an aerial refueling point a few hours later. SAC, in fact, must know global weather day by day througout the year to operate efficiently. From the detached hum of computers in NWP to the safeguarding of the country by round-the-clock air-retaliation forces seems a long step. In reality, these two aspects of our lives are as close as though they were inches rather than miles apart.

Each day NWP sends out over the facsimile circuits twenty-six prognostic charts for use by field stations, military and naval units. In addition, twelve analyses of current weather are transmitted.

Fantastic as the automatic computer operation appears, it in no way replaces the human brains directing it. All any computer can do is what it is told. The Numerical Prediction skywatchers check their results constantly to improve the selection of data to be fed into the computers. Each forecast that comes from NWP is reviewed by the nation's top forecasters to see how accurately the job was done. To make automatic forecasting as accurate as that of experts is difficult. The years of experience, the imagination and the subconscious assessment of weather measurements all forecasters employ must be reduced to mathematical form before anyone can tell a computer what to do.

Even the basic formulas now used are not entirely accurate. Many are derived from the physics of liquids, so-called hydrodynamic equations. And while air and water both are fluids, they have great differences. Chief of these is that a gas or mixture of gases like the air is compressible while water and most other liquids are, by comparison, nearly incompressible. This means that large errors may be expected by taking hydrodynamic equations and applying them without qualification to the atmosphere. Friction forces, expansion rates, temperature changes with expansion, and a host of other relationships are not at all identical in water and air. So NWP searches continuously for better mathematical means to express the atmosphere's behavior.

Today NWP's charts sent to local stations and military units are used as overall guides and as check sheets against which a local forecaster can compare his own forecasts. It is doubtful that even with the most precise new formulas developed to foretell global weather, computers will ever be capable of accounting for every local weather variation on the face of the globe. For this reason, the local skywatcher always will modify the global forecast and relate it to his experience in his particular part of the world. To continent-spanning military craft and missiles, NWP will supply increasingly accurate information for upper-air weather. The computers will hum at a faster rate and as new formulas are evolved, air flow, temperature, pressure and humidity at all altitudes over the globe will be spread almost instantly on maps to guide men's decisions and great aerial operations thousands of miles away.

CHAPTER 4

Measuring and Drawing the Sky

OVER THE northern hemisphere lie more than two billion cubic miles of air. To know and understand the actions of this vast sea of gases is the primary concern of skywatchers. For years it has been believed that the atmosphere was divided into a relatively few, distinct layers. The outer edge was not sharply defined and was generally placed "several hundred miles above the earth." Until recently this outer edge of the atmospheric envelope appeared unimportant.

The lowest layer of the atmosphere, the troposphere, extends about ten miles above the earth, slightly more than 50,000 feet. The boundary between this layer and the next is called the tropopause and is determined by temperature variations. Above this shifting boundary and extending outward another ten miles lies the stratosphere. Beyond it begins the ionosphere, a region which, because of its electrical properties, serves as a reflecting medium for radio communication between stations so far apart that the earth's curvature prevents straight line transmission. It was believed to reach nearly 600 miles above the earth. Beyond the ionosphere lay a rather vaguely defined exosphere, a region about which little was directly known.

Our recently orbited satellites have gained new and startling knowledge of what actually exists in regions high above the earth. Even the 1957 discovery of the Van Allen radiation belts has been replaced by more complete and quite different knowledge. Our satellite, Explorer XII, has sent back data that leads scientists now to believe that a single great radiation band, shaped much like a doughnut, surrounds the earth as though it fitted over our globe with the inner sides of the doughnut hole pressing against the equator. Over the poles this radiation belt does not exist but it extends outward into space some 40,000 miles directly over the equator. Recently termed the magnetosphere, it appears to be composed of dissociated protons and electrons. Early reports indicate that the magnetosphere plays a major role in aiding or hindering transmission of solar energy to the earth, which affects the weather in everyone's backyard.

Beyond the magnetosphere lies a region of great turbulence extending perhaps another 12,000 miles into space. Here, changing magnetic fields and solar winds herald the beginning of outer space as we now conceive it.

This, then, is the picture we so far have drawn of the layers of our atmosphere. Further investigation will modify even this advanced picture and it may alter the concept radically.

The composition of the atmosphere was once believed to be quite well known, too—just as the layers of it were considered known. But again the whole picture has changed with the new knowledge we have received.

Now we believe that up to 72 miles above the earth the air is composed, by volume, of 78 per cent nitrogen—a relatively inert gas—21 per cent oxygen, and up to 1 per cent of argon.

Other constituents making up less than .01 per cent are carbon dioxide, neon, helium, krypton, xenon, ozone, methane and water vapor. This mixture of gases has been known to exist for many years. What lies above it is newly discovered. Again from satellite information we know that beyond the 72-mile range and extending to as much as 600 miles above the earth is a layer of oxygen. Beyond that is a layer of helium some 300 miles thick. Beginning at around 1500 miles above the earth and extending to some 6000 miles is a layer of hydrogen. Its density decreases toward the outer edges of the layer until it mingles and is scarcely distinguishable from interplanetary gases in space.

How these newly discovered layers of gas and radiation affect the weather on the surface of the earth, we do not yet fully know. All the new information will be assimilated eventually and may possibly serve as a foundation for new theories in skywatchers' endless quest to understand and predict both weather and climate.

The present general method of picturing and measuring weather is known as the air mass technique. The theories on which it rests first were developed by a Norwegian named Karl Bjerknes in the latter part of the nineteenth century. Following Bjerknes' leadership, two generations of his sons carried on the development of the theory. It was introduced into the United States in the 1930s and soon superseded all other theories of day-to-day forecasting. Like most new theories, however, it wasn't accepted without opposition. But it worked so effectively that before long all the world's meteorologists realized it was a new and powerful tool that they had to consider.

Essentially the theory rests on the location and tracking of great masses of similarly constructed air—that is, air having nearly the same temperature and water-vapor content throughout. These masses moved in response to many factors, including the rotation of the earth, the pressure differences between them, and the presence of large bodies of water or great mountain ranges beneath them. Where these air masses of differing composition met, lines of meeting or "fronts" formed. These lines produced much of the changeable local weather we experience both summer and winter. An understanding of the air masses and the fronts between them was the keystone in the arch of the Bjerknes' theory.

Origin and Names of Air Masses

By definition, an air mass contains air having very nearly the same temperature and moisture conditions throughout. But what gives them their particular conditions depends on where they come from. Skywatchers have developed symbols and names for these great masses, some of which are large enough to straddle the continent.

In the northern hemisphere over the United States we frequently find a mass of air coming from the polar regions. It may originate over Canada or over the northern Pacific Ocean. If it comes from Canada, it is termed continental polar and designated cP. If it comes from over the ocean, it is titled maritime polar and labeled mP. Of the two, the maritime air mass probably has more moisture, since it lingered over the ocean, and even in very cold weather picked up more water vapor than the mass building up over Canada. Maritime air masses, then, are expected to be more moist, to bring more snow in the winter or rain in the summer. Another source of polar air masses is the North Atlantic Ocean. This source rarely sends its cold, moist air to any part of the United States save New England. It, too, is labeled mP.

The other great source of air masses entering or affecting the United States lies to the south. In the Pacific Ocean, the Gulf of Mexico and the Atlantic Ocean south and east of Florida large, warm and very moist masses of air move north. All are termed maritime tropical and symbolized mT. From the great land area of Mexico come other tropical air masses but they, originating over land, are termed continental tropical and designated cT.

To further specify what the characteristics of these air masses are a third letter is added to the symbol which completes it and tells whether the air mass is warm or cold. Although it may be thought that all polar air would be cold and all tropical air warm, it is a relative matter, decided in this manner: If the air is colder than the ground over which it is passing, it is designated as a cold air mass; if warmer, a warm air mass. Thus, if a maritime polar air mass comes eastward from the Pacific during the winter months when land surface in the northern United States generally is colder than the ocean to the west, the designation would be maritime polar warm, mPw. If a continental polar air mass came down from Canada during the spring months bearing very cold air it would be termed continental polar cold and labeled cPk—the "k" for cold avoids confusion with "c" for continental and was selected for use by the Bureau because it is the initial letter from the German word for cold, kalt.

Of course all air masses are modified in temperature and moisture content by the ground they pass over. But often they retain their original character for many days, affecting, in fact, *being* the weather for the land surface beneath them.

Everyone has experienced what skywatchers call air mass weather. It can be the same for as long as a week, if the air mass is large and is moving slowly. During winter months, a two- or three-day period of clear cold weather indicates that the affected locality is within a homogenous air mass—probably polar continental. During the summer, a similar air mass would bring a few days of relief from an August hot spell. But if, during those summer days, a maritime tropical air mass moves north over land areas of the United States, it could bring hot, muggy and rainy weather for several days. In either event, air mass weather changes slowly in comparison to frontal weather which changes rapidly and draws everyone's attention.

Fronts: Cold, Warm, Occluded

Fronts are the boundaries between air masses and they are often rather sharp divisions. On one side of a front, winds and precipitation and temperatures are one thing, on the other side, quite another. Many people have witnessed the passing of a front without knowing what actually was occurring. The sudden cold after summer thunder showers often signals a front passing. The abrupt change of wind direction is another indication that a front has passed just as the skywatchers at Idlewild noted by the flag being blown in the opposite direction when the occluded front went over "on schedule."

Cold Fronts

Where a mass of cold air runs into a mass of warm air and pushes the warm air upward, there exists a cold front. The cold air is heavier than warm air and, moving with more force and speed than the warm air, it will act almost like a wall moving horizontally across the surface, thrusting the warm air upward. Cold fronts usually move rather rapidly and they can, with their sudden and intense temperature changes, bring disaster to farmers and fruit growers. The fronts, of course, are not straight lines across the landscape but usually are curved, reflecting the shapes of the colliding air masses.

Warm Fronts

Warm fronts usually move much slower than cold ones and are formed when warm, usually moist air masses run into cold ones and almost literally climb on their backs. Given a greater force and speed than the cold mass, the warm one dominates but, being composed of less dense air, cannot force the cold air up. The only possible course is to rise over the cold air.

Occasionally a warm front headed in one direction will meet a cold one headed oppositely. The result is termed a stationary front and it remains that way—stationary—until the stronger of the two systems manages to overpower the other and dominate the scene.

Occluded Fronts

In the northern hemisphere, winds about a high-pressure mass of cold air flow in a clockwise direction. This flow is governed by a number of factors, among them the effect of the earth's rotation, the tendency of the high-pressure air to flow to lower-pressure levels and the Coriolis effect well known to professional skywatchers. The opposite is true of low-pressure air often associated with warm, moist tropical air masses. That is, their winds turn counterclockwise. If two such air masses bump one another the line of their meeting can often have parallel winds on either side of the boundary. This, in turn, leads to a curious situation peculiar to middle latitudes wherein the United States lies. A cyclonic low-pressure center develops which could be likened to the whorl of water escaping down a drain. The warm moist air mass establishes a warm front to one side of this center, moving counterclockwise. The cold front begins to follow the warm front. Since cold fronts move more rapidly, the cold one eventually catches the warm one, pushing the moisture-laden air upward. Much precipitation results from this overrunning of one front by the other and sky-watchers have given the phenomenon the name of an occlusion.

Clouds as Weather Indicators

Particular cloud formations are associated with frontal activity and the experienced amateur or professional skywatcher can learn much from this single observation. Of course, air mass weather often contains clouds, too: the endless battalions of fleecy, white, summer clouds all at the same altitude or the days of gray, overcast weather with constant drizzle. But frontal cloud development is so striking that nearly anyone can recognize the approach of such a weather change—particularly a cold front.

Clouds are classified by their altitude, shape, and whether they are about to release moisture or not.

Highest clouds are termed cirrus. They actually are masses of ice crystals 20,000 or more feet above the earth which appear sometimes as wisps and often in well-defined bands. "Mares' tails" is a colloquial name applied to these clouds.

Cirrostratus is a layer of high clouds of ice crystals, again above 20,000 feet, and often so thin that the sun shines easily through them making the sky itself appear white. Halos around the sun are sometimes seen in these clouds.

Cirrocumulus represent another type of high cloud and the word cumulus means vertically developed, that is, formed by upward-moving currents of air and having a puffy appearance. At high altitudes this type appears as broken layers of clouds but each cloud has a definite roundness. The patterns they make have earned them the name of "mackerel sky."

Middle clouds ranging in altitude from about 6000 to 20,000 feet are termed "alto." Still high, they are further classified as either vertically developed patches of altocumulus or thick, sun-hiding, smooth layers known as altostratus.

Lowest of the clouds may range from nearly the surface of the earth to the beginning of the alto cloud range. Simple stratus clouds of the lowest type are smooth layers of clouds showing little turbulence. Stratocumulus are low clouds, often closely grouped, with a rounded appearence. Sometimes they appear in broken patches or alone, leaving the observer able to view whatever higher clouds exist at upper elevations. Nimbostratus clouds are often black or dark gray and are filled nearly to capacity with moisture. The prefix nimbo indicates these are clouds from which rain may soon fall by the proverbial bucketfuls.

A type of cloud that reaches from as low as 1500 feet and can tower to heights around 40,000 feet is the cumulus cloud. In the more advanced phase of such a cloud's development, it takes on the name cumulonimbus and is the familiar thunderhead, visible most often on hot summer days, though they develop at all seasons of the year and may often be hidden by other cloud formations.

Some of these clouds are associated with cold fronts and some with warm fronts. When a cold front is moving into a region, it often is heralded first by the feathery cirrus clouds, and then by the appearance of a line of cumulus clouds stretching along the front. If this cold front is severe, the cumulus clouds may already be approaching the cumulonimbus stage and the bank of clouds then is termed a squall line. The flat, dark bases of all the clouds appear to be at the same altitude, the roiling upward rolls of cloud often show rapid movement and high near the top of them the cloud spreads out forming what frequently is called an anvil top. The feathery cirrus clouds that come first over the horizon represent the forward edges of this flat-topped cloud structure. Cold fronts move at an average rate of between 20 and 30 miles per hour, which means that one, 200 miles away at sunset, may be on your doorstep by morning.

Warm fronts advance at a slower rate than cold fronts and often are more difficult to spot from the accompanying cloud formations. Since they are formed by warm, moist air sliding up on a cold mass of air and pushing it along, the primary cloud characteristic associated with them is a stratus development. Thus cirrostratus or altostratus clouds appearing and gradually covering the sky may indicate such a front is approaching. But the slope formed by the warm air and cold air boundary is so shallow that the first of the stratus clouds may come to view while the actual front (where the boundary between the air masses touches the ground) is a thousand miles away. This means it will take some time for the front to arrive.

But when cirrostratus clouds have been replaced by altostratus clouds, then by stratus and nimbostratus, it is a fairly safe bet that the front is near. Light rain may begin to fall before the front arrives and increase in intensity as it approaches. This is opposite to the precipitation in many cold fronts where the majority of the precipitation occurs after the front has passed.

Cloud interpretation, like any other phase of skywatching, requires practice and must be done in conjunction with other observations to make predictions about the weather in a particular location. But it does give the surface observer a means of telling which way the wind is blowing high above his head —which is itself an important signal of weather to come.

Air masses, the fronts between them and the clouds associated with the fronts are three primary measurements of the sky. But after measuring them, the skywatcher has to draw them meaningfully on a piece of paper; he must make a weather map.

Synoptic Charts

One of the most useful methods of organizing and presenting a mass of measurements is by graphing. The word graph is the scientifically accepted one meaning to picture and, although many sciences use graphs, it is doubtful if any employ them more frequently than meteorology, for a weather map is a graph. It contains more data than many graphs and requires skill and experience to interpret, but it is an essential tool in the skywatchers' work.

Outline maps of the United States, with the state boundaries shown and all the Weather Bureau and other reporting stations indicated by small circles, are printed and sent to all stations that will make their own synoptic charts. These blanks are used at a prodigous rate in larger stations like Idlewild; in the Extended Forecast Section of the National Meteorological Center, many of the blanks show the entire northern hemisphere and all the reporting stations.

Data received periodically on the teletypewriters comes in a special code agreed upon by members of the World Meteorological Organization. An experienced reader of these symbols can take a blank weather map and begin to place the data on the printed station circle, the small dot marking the existence of a reporting station. There are numbers, abbreviations and small visual symbols that can be placed in their appointed positions around the station, filling it in. To the laymen, the station circles take on a cluttered, unreadable look, but to the skywatcher the code on the charts begins to assume meaning. The information that can be crowded around one station is amazing. It tells the skywatcher all the following things:

Wind speed and direction
Barometric pressure
Net pressure change in the last three hours
Tendency of pressure change—up or down
Amount of precipitation in the last six hours
Kind of precipitation—hail, snow, rain
When precipitation began and ended—if it has ended
Height of lowest cloud base
Amount of sky coverage of lowest clouds ($\frac{2}{10}$, $\frac{7}{10}$, etc.)
Type of low clouds (stratus, nimbostratus, etc.)
Type of middle cloud development
Direction of motion of middle clouds
Amount of total sky coverage

Visibility in miles on the surface
Present state of the weather
Surface temperature
The dew point

When all of this information has been transferred from code on a teletypewriter sheet to code, number and symbol on the station circles of all reporting stations, the skywatcher is ready to build his map. Of course, he already has much data to read and from which he can draw some conclusions. But he is not finished.

With the air mass technique of weather analysis, the location of the centers of high and low pressure—the centers of the air masses—is critical. To place these on the map, the meteorologist begins to draw the isobars or lines of equal pressure. As contour maps of the earth's surface reveal hills and valleys, so the isobars, when drawn, show the hills of high pressure and the valleys of low pressure.

An isobar is a line joining points of equal barometric pressure and if, say, the 1020 millibar line is needed, the map maker searches for two stations one of which has a pressure above 1020 and one below it. Let us say he locates two adjacent stations, one with an adjusted pressure reading of 1016 and the other with an adjusted pressure of 1022. Somewhere between them lies a point where the pressure is 1020. To locate it the weatherman takes the difference between the two station readings, which is six millibars, and marks a point on a line between the two station circles a proportionate distance from one or the other station. His six millibar difference is considered to change at a constant rate between the stations. The 1020 point he searches for must lie four sixths of the way from the 1016 station or two sixths of the distance from the 1022 station. The entire process, of course, is called interpolation and the sky-watcher skilled in drawing maps soon scarcely has to think out the proportion he wants. Reading the pressures at many stations at almost the same instant, he sees where the 1020 millibar line will generally run and he sketches it in lightly with lead pencil. He draws the 1010 line and so on until he has produced the isobars and defined the air masses.

The isobars, wavy, curving lines across the map, encircle high- and low-pressure centers. They never cross one another (for this would indicate that two different pressures exist at the same point and this is impossible) and their only deviation from gently curving lines is where they meet a frontal line. On these front lines, the pressure shifts rapidly and it is reflected in the patterns of isobars that result.

Frontal lines themselves are drawn. Cold fronts are marked with a series of black shaded triangles spaced along the front on the side facing the direction of the frontal movement. Warm fronts are similarly marked, but with black shaded semicircles. A stationary front is marked with warm front semicircles on one side and cold front triangles on the other. An occluded front has them both on the same side placed alternately along the line.

Centers of high pressure are often marked H and those of low pressure with an L. Sometimes the source of the air is shown with the symbols indicating it is maritime or continental, polar or tropical, warm or cold.

When all the station data has been properly placed, isobars drawn and fronts indicated, the weather map is complete. The entire process for a skilled weatherman takes less than an hour.

The completed surface map is useful only until the next six hourly reports come surging from the teletypewriters. Then the process must be repeated for weather data wears out rapidly.

In addition to surface maps such as the one just described, there are maps of the upper-pressure levels. With fewer stations reporting upper-air observations, the process is somewhat simpler but still other types of maps both of the surface and upper air must also be drawn. Some are drawn to show the temperature distribution over the country and on these maps the points of equal temperature are joined by lines called isotherms. On upper-air maps, isotachs are often drawn—lines connecting points where wind speeds are equal. If isotachs and isobars must be shown on the same map, different colored inks are used to draw the finished lines. When all the maps are in and have begun to overlap one another, the skywatcher studying them begins the task of foretelling the weather by drawing yet another map, one which indicates what the weather will be in advance. These synoptic charts of present and future weather are man's best means of drawing a picture of the endlessly moving ocean of air above him.

CHAPTER 5

Origin and Growth of the Weather Bureau

MEN IN previous centuries did not have the large, coordinated organization that the Bureau Chief heads today. Meteorology, in fact, is a very young science. The government's daily bulletins and forecasts did not exist a hundred years ago. What we know today as the Weather Bureau was started on February 9, 1870, by a Congressional Resolution. It read:

"Be it resolved by the Senate and House of Representatives of the United States of America in Congress assembled, that the Secretary of War be, and he hereby is, authorized and required to provide for taking meteorological observations at the military stations in the interior of the continent and at other points in the States and Territories of the United States, and for giving notice on the northern lakes and on the seacoast, by magnetic telegraph and marine signals, of the approach and force of storms."

There had been much discussion as to what agency of the government should operate the Weather Service, as it was called. The War Department was chosen for what appeared to be two sound reasons: a network of posts existed and were manned by disciplined personnel; more important, the Army Signal Service operated an established telegraph service and this communication system linked all posts with Washington. Even in that early day it was recognized that simultaneous observations quickly assembled from many locations were a key factor in understanding weather patterns.

Much earlier than 1870, however, many men made individual efforts to gain weather data. As early as 1664 a Reverend John Campanius began making regular observations at Swedes Fort near Wilmington, Delaware. Working without instruments, however, he could do little more than describe day-to-day weather.

The first instrumental records were kept by John Lining of Charleston, South Carolina, in 1738. His instruments, of course, were crude by today's standards yet several of them bore a striking resemblance to those used today. Rain gauges were common long before John Lining's time, and although they consisted only of a simple catch bowl of some shape, they did measure the precipitation in a comparative fashion. Such devices are known to have existed for nearly 2400 years in countries where rainfall was a major factor determining the life span of the people.

The invention of the barometer is generally credited to Evangelista Torricelli, one of Galileo's students. He inverted a tube filled with mercury into an open bowl of the liquid metal and saw that a column of about thirty inches was upheld by the air. The tube he used was longer than thirty inches and as the mercury sank to its equilibrium level it produced a vacuum above the enclosed mercury in the tube. Immortality came to this Italian experimenter by having his name associated with the space above the mercury. To this day it is called the Torricelli vacuum.

Galileo himself invented the thermometer. He used water as a liquid and later alcohol. A hundred years later Daniel Fahrenheit improved the "thermoscope" as it was called by utilizing mercury.

During the years preceding simultaneous observation of weather conditions, many intellectually curious men in America took up skywatching. Thomas Jefferson and Benjamin Franklin observed and recorded data at regular intervals, and Jefferson's activities became so widely known that his friends went to him not only for political advice, but also for weather information. All who studied the weather individually recognized, as did Jefferson, that to get truly useful information would require many people at many places all observing wind direction and speed, pressure, temperature and so forth at the same instant. This, Jefferson knew, was the only thing that could put meteorology among the practical sciences from which men would derive benefit. But in those eighteenth-century days communication was slow. Mail was entrusted to passing travelers and weeks might pass before a report was delivered. It appeared hopeless to try to set up any skywatching system.

Some efforts were made nonetheless. John Lining's Charleston, South Carolina, began keeping descriptive weather records in 1670 and maintained them until 1873, when the chore was taken over by the newly formed government service. A foretaste of the use to which weather information was to be put came from this pioneering city. The early data was used to attract settlers to the colony in pamphlets written by men who must have been among the earliest civic boosters on the continent.

The first organized meteorological observations taken at more than one location were begun in 1817 by Josiah Meigs who headed the Land Office. He had three daily observations taken by the regional offices and sent to him. The Surgeon General of the Army also set up a similar organization two years later. These efforts were followed by similar ones of the Patent Office in 1841 and by the Smithsonian Institute in 1847. During this time a few states also set up skywatching networks. Perhaps the most persuasive results came from the efforts of Professor Cleveland Abbe of the Mitchel Astronomical Observatory at Cincinnati, Ohio, during the latter part of the 1860s. When the service became a part of the government Abbe was called on to help organize the infant system.

As often happens in many fields of science, a discovery or invention in one removes a great roadblock in another. The development of the electron microscope, for example, instantly became a boon to biology by enabling the life scientists to "see" particles of matter they needed to study. So, in earlier years, a development in electricity solved the problem of daily meteorological observation analysis. The principle of the telegraph— discovered and made practical by a number of workers in the field of electromagnetic inquiry—provided the answer to gathering weather data quickly from many places.

Joseph Henry, an enthusiastic electromagnetician and all-around scientist, was interested in meteorology. He saw that the telegraph could make simultaneous weather study both possible and useful. By 1849 telegraph lines linked all the major cities and towns of the United States. As the frontier moved west and railroads spearheaded the great drive, the clack of telegraph keys was the voice of the expanding nation. Henry, then Secretary of the Smithsonian Institute, leaped, figuratively at least, aboard the bandwagon. He made arrangements with the telegraph companies to have their telegraphers take weather observations and send reports to him at appointed times. Within one year he had 150 reporting stations. He apparently impressed his telegrapher-meteorologist colleagues sufficiently with the importance of rapid transmission of weather information, for it has been recorded that the data was sent as top priority material—in advance of death notices.

The Smithsonian phase of skywatching continued to expand rapidly. Five years after commencing operations, regular reports came to the Smithsonian Institute from thirty-one states and a few locations in Canada. By 1860 Henry had 500 reporting stations operating in the network. Then war, the great disrupter, shattered the working weather system and as the Southern States declared themselves independent of the Union Government, weather reports stopped coming from the South as suddenly as if someone had cut the telegraph line—which someone probably did.

What we know today as the weather map is called by meteorologists a synoptic chart (see p. 64). This unique form of weather presentation was developed in the United States by Joseph Henry when the data began pouring into his office. In effect it is a picture of the weather at one time as it exists over the country and, in Confucius' words, a picture is worth a thousand words.

When Joseph Henry began his Smithsonian weather net, the gold rush was on in California. The mountain men who had preceded the pioneers were vanishing with the beaver they sought. Wagon trains rattled over dry ground or squelched in the mud moving west of "Saint Looie." Iowa had been admitted to the Union only three years before—and a year later California would come in as a state. But in between were the territories, the roving Indians and the diminishing buffalo herds. Probing west and south along the Santa Fe Trail, west to the mountain passes in Colorado and California and northwest along the Missouri went the small detachments of the U. S. Army, the Indian Agent, the settler, the farmer, building towns and hacking farms from the wilderness. The telegraph, much to Henry's delight, began to link them all.

For many years it had been observed that weather tends to move from west to east and as the expansion of America progressed, the location of weather observation stations followed and sent back more and more useful information. Joseph Henry knew that the science of meteorology, with the help of the telegraph and the westward expansion of the nation, was on the verge of growing up. For he knew that trying to forecast for the nation from one station's observations was like trying to guess the pattern of a rug by examining one thread. Soon after starting his weather net, Joseph Henry's synoptic charts appeared in several newspapers and these were accompanied by what was then called the Probability—or Forecast.

The virtual collapse of the important Smithsonian weather net at the outbreak of the Civil War did not end interest in a national service. It merely postponed it. During the conflict little more than local forecasting was possible on either side. One man, Francis Capen, offered his services to President Lincoln as a forecaster. His idea was sound but his training was weak. President Lincoln turned down Capen's offer to benefit the Union cause by saving lives and, as Capen put it, "millions of dollars." Of Capen's request for a referral to the War Department, Lincoln said, "It seems to me Mr. Capen knows nothing about the weather, in advance. He told me three days ago that it would not rain again until the 30th of April or 1st of May. It is raining now and has been for ten hours. I cannot spare any more time to Mr. Capen."

When peace returned to the United States, pressure grew for the establishment of a national weather service. It came from chambers of commerce in New York and the Midwest. In Wisconsin and Illinois regional efforts had convinced some important businessmen that such a governmental service would save a great deal of loss, not only of crops, but also of ships and men and goods being transported on the Great Lakes and the rivers of the nation. A congressman, Representative H. E. Paine of Wisconsin, was finally persuaded to introduce the important resolution. The bill passed Congress on February 2, 1870, and was signed by President Grant on February 9.

The Signal Service was entrusted with taking the weather observations. The men were trained telegraphers and it was thought they could double as weather observers while standing a watch by a telegraph key. General A. J. Myer as Chief Signal Officer thereby became the first Chief of the Weather Bureau as we know it today.

With twenty-four stations reporting on November 1, 1870, the first reports came to Washington. They were placed on a synoptic chart and the forecast made. Within two hours regional forecasts were on the wires and the operation was underway.

At first it failed to interest the public. Initially newspapers shied away from the free weather reports and inevitable mistakes in forecasting for certain areas brought sharp criticisms. In one case a forecast called for a killing frost in a tobacco-growing region. It did not reach the farmers in time and crops were ruined. Investigation of the incident showed that the telegraph operator held up the message until it was too late to be useful. By 1890 the Signal Service had 178 stations reporting. Not all were completely equipped, however. The first fully equipped stations had a barometer, hygrometer, thermometer, anemometer, wind vane, rain gauge, a clock and tool box, plus pads of forms for record keeping. Less well-equipped, or third-order stations, had instruments enough only to report maximum and minimum temperatures daily and the amount of precipitation.

Inevitably, as the years passed, public interest in forecasts mounted and whenever a cold front was successfully tracked, those who benefited became interested in the Weather Service's efforts. These efforts expanded as the nation continued to grow. In 1871 the Weather Service began observing rivers and issuing warnings of flood stages. Storm-signal flags came into use. In 1885 the Service, working with the British Meteorological Office, began sending out storm warnings for the Atlantic shipping lanes. In 1884 special reports to cotton and sugar growers became a regular feature.

To help make observations, volunteer skywatchers early augmented the regular stations. The Smithsonian's 383 cooperative observers—the remnant of Henry's network—were transferred to Signal Service control. No question remained in anyone's mind but that the daily reporting of weather was a permanent feature of our national life.

As facilities spread, forecasters in such locations as St. Paul, New York and San Francisco received permission to make local area forecasts. If the local predictions fell below acceptable percentages of accuracy, however, Washington withdrew the privilege. Accuracy was high on a national level. It reached 80 per cent and experienced meteorologists like Joseph Henry and Cleveland Abbe hoped for 85 or 90 per cent accuracy as the network expanded.

Research under Cleveland Abbe, who had joined the Weather Service, made progress and although this little publicized phase of work was in its infancy, he investigated a number of phenomena we still are studying today: moisture in the atmosphere, electrical disturbances and tornadoes.

Progress in skywatching did not proceed placidly under the Signal Service, however. Army-civilian friction which had existed from the start, sprang into prominence with the indictment of a Captain Henry Howgate for the embezzlement of Weather Service funds. The specific amount in the indictment was $90,000 although some of the investigators put the sum closer to $237,000. In retaliation, Congress lowered appropriations during the following years. This expected political reprisal decreased the efficiency of the Service to such an extent that complaints began to pile up. It became evident to many officers as well as civilians that transfer of the Weather Service to civilian control might quiet critics and allow the Service to operate efficiently once more. Unquestionably, a professional group of meteorologists could best cope with the problem—

and they would not be distracted from their work by other duties as was often the case with Army personnel. On July 1, 1891, the Weather Service was transferred to the Department of Agriculture.

At the time, what was to become the Weather Bureau performed all its functions primarily from the Washington office with the aid of only four forecasters. But as the nation grew and the population spread westward and filled the great plains with settlements, the task became too great for a central office and only four forecasters. By 1894 forty forecasters were at work and the functions of the Washington office had been decentralized.

Many meteorologists believed that with these improvements the practical limit of forecasting had been reached. But the time soon came to add another dimension to the measurement of the atmosphere. The direction was up. Surface observations had yielded nearly all the secrets that the instruments of that age could unlock.

The idea of taking upper-air soundings was not new but it had been tried only at great intervals and in isolated positions. The earliest ascents were manned balloons filled with hydogen, one of which had been accomplished successfully in 1784. During the 1870s and 1880s meteorologists both in the United States and in Europe had gone up laden with instruments to bring down information about the sea of air above the earth. But there were many drawbacks to this method, not the least of which was the expense. One flight was costly enough, but the idea of sending many flights up was so fantastically expensive that only a few men dreamed it might take place on a daily basis at many stations throughout the country. Readings from such high-surface locations as Mt. Washington, New Hampshire, had not proved to be the answer. Even the highest mountains didn't go up far enough nor were there enough of them scattered over the land to meet the skywatchers' demands.

An outstanding meteorologist, Professor Charles Marvin, reported to the Department of Agriculture in 1897 that upper-air soundings would have to become a daily feature of the Bureau's work. The question remained: How to do it? Marvin himself had experimented with box kites carrying instruments up toward the desired levels but these were not too successful since it required at least a ten-mile-per-hour wind to fly the kite. Nonetheless, Professor Marvin persisted and in 1898 the simultaneous flying of kites from seventeen stations gave the first reading of the upper atmosphere from which meteorologists could draw the profile of the air.

The chief value of these upper-air observations at the time was that they gave the meteorologists a look at the larger air motions, motions not influenced by local surface conditions. No small line of hills or series of lakes or hot fields distort the pressures at high altitudes. In the upper air the motion observed comes from larger, more fundamental sources: the sun, the earth's rotation, the polar regions and the distribution of large bodies of water over the hemisphere's surface. Interesting as all this was to the meteorologist, it held no fascination for the average citizen walking about on the bottom of the sea of air. No fascination, that is, until average citizens began flying through that air at altitudes of ten, twenty and thirty thousand feet.

The invention of the airplane has done as much to spur weather research as anything since the beginnings of the science. Orville and Wilbur Wright who first began experimenting with kites to carry a man aloft, at last turned their investigations to the development of a motor and wings to do the job. But their canvas and wood contraptions were as much a prey of winds and turbulence as any kite. They had to know about the weather. For information, Wilbur Wright wrote to Professor Marvin, who later was to become Chief of the Bureau. Still laboring in their bicycle shop in Dayton, Ohio, the Wrights asked for wind velocities in the vicinity of Chicago during the usual August, September, October period with, if possible, daily maximums and minimums. The Bureau obliged and sent copies of the *Monthly Weather Review* containing the data gathered for that period the year before.

When the Wrights went to North Carolina, they relied on the nearest Bureau station for a while and then, having moved too far from it to use its winds for a local forecast, bought their own anemometer and made their own observations.

Essentially, of course, these pioneer flights of the Wright brothers, as well as those of such others as Octave Chanute, used surface-wind information but as aviation grew into a major military and economic force, upper-air observations became of great importance.

Kites first used by Marvin soon gave way to free unmanned balloons and eventually means were developed to send radios aloft which could transmit information to ground stations—radiosonde in its crude state emerged. With the development of radio direction-finding equipment, the latest link was forged. Stations like those at Caribou now contribute data to synoptic charts which can be drawn up to and beyond the tropopause.

A unique feature of the Weather Bureau throughout its history has been the existence of a large group of volunteer observers—amateur skywatchers—who receive no pay for their work. Their reports come from locations not covered by regular stations and they fill in great gaps in the weather picture over the country. The origin of these cooperative observers, as the Bureau terms them, lies in Joseph Henry's Smithsonian Institute network. The men he recruited to make observations were all unpaid volunteers and when they "transferred" to the Signal Corps, they retained their volunteer status. In the early days lack of equipment often hampered the efforts of these observers—a lack that scarcely needs detailing when the Secretary of War was allowed to spend no more than fifteen dollars per county to equip them. One out of three of these observers did not have a rain gauge or thermometer.

The value of early cooperative observers' reports was largely in the field of climatology rather than day-to-day meteorology. Still, they kept an eye on river stages and mailed in reports of temperature and outstanding weather phenomena such as severe frosts. Under the administration of Willis Moore, the Bureau reorganized stations and volunteers during the period from 1896 to 1913. By then there were 4200 working volunteers.

For many years the question of the best time to make simultaneous observations had plagued even the professional meteorologists and a rigid schedule—whatever it might be—could scarcely be enforced on payless volunteers. In 1882, the scheme was to take readings at seven in the morning, two in the afternoon and nine at night. But many volunteers, perhaps feeling that seven was a bit too early to get up, settled for 8:00 A.M. This inconsistency, of course, robbed observations of simultaneity. In one community an observer would note temperature

DISCARD

at 8:00 A.M., a neighboring skywatcher would choose 9:00 A.M. while still another would comply with the system and read his thermometer at 7:00 A.M. It must be added, however, that even the most professional of meteorologists at a meeting of the International Meteorological Conference in Munich in 1891 could not agree on an observation schedule that satisfied all representatives. Today, far from being overshadowed by the professional completely, the cooperative observer has become an increasingly useful member of the network and his ranks have swelled to 12,000. This amateur skywatcher may go unpaid by his government but he doesn't go unappreciated. Annual awards are presented to members of the cooperative corps who have made unusual contributions during the year. In 1961 five Thomas Jefferson Awards (so named because of Jefferson's interest in the science) went to volunteer observers and twenty-four John Campanius Holm awards were given to citizens from Chugwater, Wyoming to Chewsville, Maryland. Dr. Reichelderfer in announcing the awards emphasized the importance of the volunteers. "The cooperative observer program," he said, "has been in existence longer than the Weather Bureau itself, and many families of observers have been collecting weather data for generations. The information provided by these observers has been of inestimable value to the nation."

Until the beginning of the twentieth century, the Weather Bureau—like the nation itself—was preoccupied with western expansion. For the Bureau this meant continual addition of new stations to span the continent and fill the blank places on the weather maps. But even in those times, the meteorologists knew that the sea lanes to Europe, crowded as they were with

DISCARD

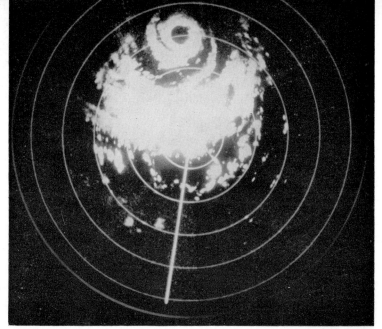

A radar portrait of 1961's Hurricane Carla pinpoints the giant storm 150 miles off the Texas coast. Bureau stations from Maine to the Gulf keep constant watch during the hurricane season and help produce earlier warnings.

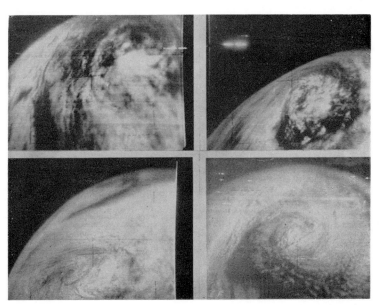

Photographs of a great storm center taken by weather satellite Tiros show clockwise whorl of clouds about a low-pressure center in the southern hemisphere. In the northern hemisphere they rotate counterclockwise.

Famed Bureau station atop Mt. Washington, N.H., experiences as rapid and severe weather changes as any United States station. At an altitude of 6288 feet, the summit has sub-arctic climate, a brief summer season.

Nature's most violent storm, a tornado, brings nearly total destruction where it strikes. Bureau records show these storms occur most frequently in the midwest during May and June, but may strike anywhere, any time.

Dramatic lightning displays like this often accompany thunderstorms formed along advancing cold fronts. More intense discharges accompany tornado weather. A measure of this intensity helps skywatchers locate tornado conditions and permits early warning of communities.

A radar-equipped Navy plane flies toward a hurricane at sea. These long-range planes penetrate a tropical storm and measure its size and force. Constant surveillance by aircraft allows no storm to approach the United States undetected.

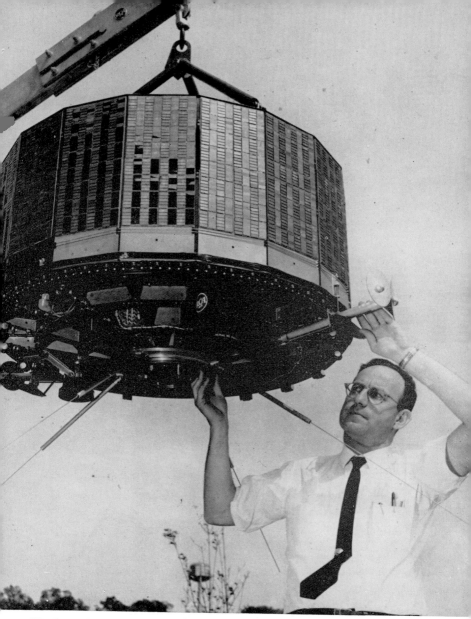

Weather satellite Tiros, a version of which now circles the earth sending back photographs, weather data and cosmic ray information, gives skywatchers a long-dreamed-of weather station in the sky. As old satellites run out of power, new, modified ones are sent aloft to continue work.

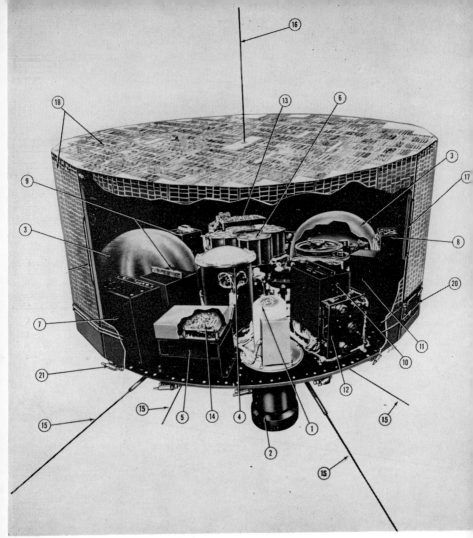

This cutaway drawing of Tiros, the weather satellite, shows its miniaturized components. 1) One of two TV cameras; 2) wide-angle camera lens; 3) tape recorders; 4) electronic timer; 5) TV transmitter; 6) chemical batteries; 7) camera electronics; 8) tape recorder electronics; 9) control circuits; 10) auxiliary controls; 11) power converter; 12) voltage regulator; 13) battery charging regulator; 14) auxiliary synchronizing generator for TV; 15) transmitting antennas; 16) receiving antenna; 17) solar sensor to relate position of satellite to the sun; 18) solar cells; 20) de-spin mechanism; 21) spin-up rockets.

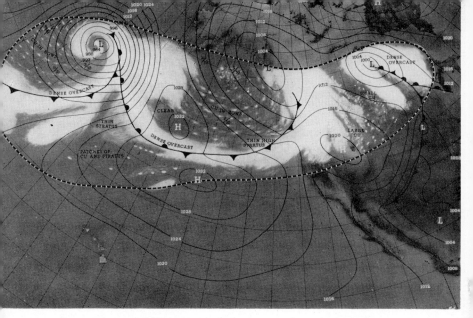

Storm family over the North Pacific Ocean. Tiros cloud pictures superimposed on conventional weather map.

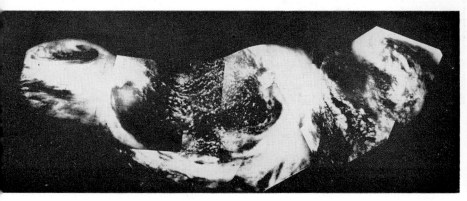

Actual Tiros photographs taken on May 20, 1960.

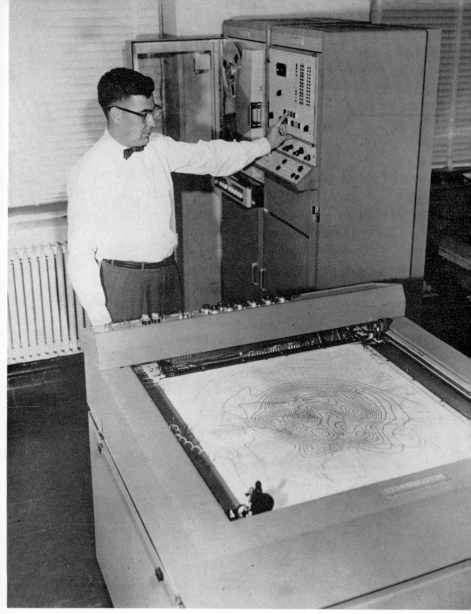

A National Meteorological Center computer (background) directs an automatic map plotter to draw a weather map of the entire northern hemisphere. System requires no human intervention, takes less than three minutes to do the job.

shipping, could give much data to the growing science of meteorology. The European countries themselves, of course, were directly concerned, for the weather formed over the Atlantic eventually reached their boundaries. Actually, while he headed the Bureau, Willis Moore suggested that ships could be used as oceanic weather stations. When radio communication became a reliable reality some ships did report extreme disturbances, but not until aviation began to ride on the air above the ocean did anyone seriously tackle the problem.

Men had made attempts to make aviation forecasts over the Atlantic Ocean but the information far from land was meager and only the most general terms could be employed. Then, in 1919, as the Navy prepared to send three planes on a trans-Atlantic flight to Portugal by way of Newfoundland and the Azores, meteorologists contributed their skill to the venture. Dr. Reichelderfer went to Portugal while another skywatcher journeyed to Newfoundland. The man in Newfoundland radioed his observations to Washington. He correctly forewarned of poor visibility near the Azores but despite this information, two Navy planes crashed. Only one reached Portugal safely— the first airplane to fly from the new world to the old.

Not until World War II did Moore's dream of permanent Atlantic weather stations become a reality. In that conflict, Coast Guard ships were stationed at critical weather points along the northern sea lanes where they circled endlessly as floating weather stations. Weather Bureau observers on board made the usual surface observations, and took upper-air soundings every six hours. These wartime experiments proved so useful that after the war the Bureau, in cooperation with the Coast Guard, set up a network of eight ship stations. It required twenty-seven vessels to maintain continuous observation. This was an expensive operation. Where a shore station cost about $60,000 annually, the expense of each ocean-going station was approximately $600,000. Other nations benefited from the United States' scheme since all information became available to the World Meteorological Organization. As transatlantic air traffic increased the reporting stations became even more important. Then, in 1952, a governmental economy drive threatened the entire project and worried meteorologists consulted with other interested nations: Canada, Great Britain, France and Norway. They agreed to help share the cost of the ocean network. It operates today to safeguard lives over this heavily traveled region of the globe.

The Pacific Ocean doesn't carry or underlie as much concentrated traffic. It has a few stations of the same sort but even so there are many areas where weather on the surface or aloft is not measured. Instead of filling the Pacific with stations, the Bureau has turned in a northerly direction, looking to the Arctic regions. Much of the weather in the northern United States is influenced by Arctic temperatures and winds. As wartime flight operations probed farther north, the Bureau went along and today it has stations on Newfoundland. Cooperative stations also are manned by Air Force and Bureau personnel in Canada and Greenland.

Weather today is a hemispheric problem and the Bureau receives thousands of reports every twenty-four hours from all over the world. They come from 315 regular stations in or near the United States; 148 upper-air weather-sounding stations, 97 radar stations, 22 automatic weather stations, 12,-000 cooperative observers plus another 485 stations under the

Federal Aviation Agency and private airlines. More than 3000 ships at sea send in data and, on top of all, data comes from 2000 stations outside the United States over the northern hemisphere.

Could they see the great organization they had helped to build, Joseph Henry, Cleveland Abbe, Charles Marvin and Willis Moore and many others probably would blink in amazement. Unquestionably, they would compare the present modern organization with their early efforts to send up kites here and there to plumb the ocean of air or think ruefully of their efforts to persuade Signal Corps telegraphers to run out and look at the thermometer at the proper time.

The Bureau today has modernized the methods of distributing weather information to the vast public it serves. In place of reports that read "A decided diminution (in pressure) has appeared unannounced in Missouri accompanied with a rapid rise in the thermometer. . . ." the public watches pretty weather girls on TV and listens to weather jingles on the radio. While these methods and some of the reporting make veteran skywatchers wince, they know that some of the information is getting across.

For those citizens who do not want to wait for weather reports via radio or television, especially taped recordings are fed continuously to telephone subscribers in eleven major cities. All a curious citizen must do is dial WEather 1212, or a similar number, and he receives the latest weather information without glancing out the window. Every hour the forecast is revised. A telephone company "weather room" is linked to the nearest Bureau station by teletypewriter and telephone. Telephone company employees make a new recording and any subscriber has weather information at his finger-tips, never more than an hour old.

Will it rain? Will the snow stop? Is it going to be cold this weekend? Should we plan a trip? These questions prompt 205,000,000 telephone calls a year.

CHAPTER 6

Service to the Public

EARLY IN September, 1961, Hurricane Carla, described as one of the most severe storms ever to strike the United States, became a notation on weather-station maps. Aircraft tracked the growing storm until it was picked up on radar 200 miles from the Texas coast. The storm quite literally could do nothing without being seen by observers even though it still remained far from land. It not only was seen and reported by radar observers, its growing strength and increasing winds were reported by an automatic observation station bobbing at its mooring far out in the Gulf of Mexico. As if such watchfulness were not enough, the weather satellite Tiros III busily took pictures of the hurricane each time the satellite passed over the storm area high above the earth. As the monster storm grew and curved northward toward the coast, a special network began to send hurricane observations to Weather Bureau forecast centers. Planes from Navy and Air Force installations were flown inland away from the predicted path. Civil defense officials, fire, police and national guard units prepared shelters and escape routes.

Long before the storm struck, weathermen knew it was a

record disturbance. Winds of 150 miles per hour, sweeping out a great circular path, set a record before the storm hit the coast. The intense disturbance measured 500 miles in diameter.

The shore toward which Carla aimed was a low, swampy coast where a few feet of abnormal tide could cause destructive floods over hundreds of square miles of bayou country. There, in remote settlements and on individual farms, people would die unless they could be evacuated. Farther inland the danger would come from torrential rains as Carla's moisture-laden air moved in and began to drop tons of water into shallow creek beds, soaking the ground and surpassing the capacity of the soil to absorb the moisture. Then a runoff of flood proportions would wreak havoc over a wider area, sweeping everything before it.

In another, more primitive day a storm like Carla would have claimed thousands of lives. Before radio, radar or the birth of the special Hurricane Warning system none but weather-wise natives would have known of the storm's approach and even they, with the best rule-of-thumb knowledge in the world, would have had no way to gauge its severity. As it turned out, the loss of life in Carla came largely in primitive areas where the people believed that their homes which had survived previous storms would survive this one. Many didn't.

Heeding the warnings of the Weather Bureau, people in cities and towns along the coast and in low-lying areas began the largest temporary evacuation in the history of the United States. They took only the barest necessities and hurried to places where they could escape the worst of the tides and razing wind. Every available shelter in the communities receiving the displaced people was opened and the refugee-struck towns were strained to feed and care for the evacuees. The experience of all concerned in the mass escape was unique. The last stragglers were leaving the danger area when Carla struck the coast. Onshore winds from the right-hand half of the circular storm piled water on the shore and swept it far up into the channels and bayous, taking houses and docks and boats as it went. Winds of more than 200 mph completed the initial damage and then the storm moved inland. Literally tons of water fell from the skies, farther and farther north, bringing disastrous floods to communities hundreds of miles from the coast.

When the storm passed into history and the displaced people returned to their homes, it is possible that some of them mentally thanked the Weather Bureau for its accurate and early warnings. What they did not know was that the warnings were part of a routine operation. Not routine, however, was the storm—the most monstrous hurricane in modern Weather Bureau history.

Hurricane Warning Service

The Bureau's special interest in hurricanes goes back at least to 1896. Before that year the need for special observation stations was fully recognized but funds and personnel were lacking. Historical records, dated as far back as the discovery of the New World, indicated that hurricanes regularly struck the Lesser Antilles, the Central American coast and the coast of what has since become the United States. In fact, the very name hurricane is our adaptation of ancient Caribbean and South American Indian names, all remarkably similar in general pronunciation for such storms. Early meteorologists showed great interest in these storms but were powerless to do anything about finding out where they came from, how they originated or what path they would follow. To single observers on the affected islands or coasts, any plot of past hurricane paths gave no clue to the path or speed or ferocity of the next one. The storms seemed to originate north of the equator and either far east across the Atlantic (near the Cape Verde Islands), off the northeast coast of South America, or in the southwestern section of the Gulf of Mexico. Their paths might be due west, or northwest or north or northeast. They might even describe huge circles, doubling back on themselves. But in the days before 1896, little could be done to keep track of them.

Under Bureau Chief Willis Moore, however, the present Hurricane Warning Service got its start. The lever that pried funds from Congress was a hurricane which, in 1896, struck the eastern coast of the United States in Florida and moved north over the land to Pennsylvania. It killed 114 people and caused $7,000,000 damage. Goaded by Moore and the advent of the Spanish American War, funds were forthcoming to set up several stations in the West Indies with headquarters in Havana. The first three such stations managed to forewarn of several storms, but Moore knew that the stations were so widely spaced that a full-sized hurricane could slip through the thin net without being detected. From 1898 onward, special reports during the height of the hurricane season—July to October—were included in the daily weather maps sent out by Washington. By 1901 the special network of stations—still located in the islands of the Caribbean—numbered sixteen. The observers in these stations, nearly all of which were one-man outposts, tried to get information from the French on Martinique and the British from their islands of Nassau and Barbados as well as from several Mexican stations. They also asked steamships to radio storm conditions when they met them, but since weather-wise captains avoided storm paths as much as possible this maritime information remained scanty.

As the population of the United States grew, storms striking the coasts caused more and more damage and took a greater toll of lives. The famous Galveston hurricane of September, 1900, claimed an estimated 6000 lives and Moore's requests for more funds began to receive Congressional attention. At one such hearing, when a dissenting representative irritated Chief Moore, he said, "Some day a hurricane will slip between our West Indian Stations and hit the Gulf or South Atlantic coast entirely unannounced." He couldn't have been more prophetic. The next season a hurricane struck the South Carolina coast with only four hours' warning.

One of the greatest weaknesses of the special service was the absence of information on such storms until they neared coastal areas. The forward speed and rotational wind speeds of the storm, as well as its size, all are vital in forecasting its path and severity. In 1935 the service was reorganized and the number of stations increased. A special teletype circuit linked them and they gave reports to each other and to Washington four times daily.

The first direct measurement of hurricanes came in 1943 when a military pilot deliberately flew a training plane into a storm over the Gulf of Mexico to see what it was like. He flew in and out safely enough and the scheme of penetrating hurricanes with specially equipped aircraft was born. Soon routine flights brought back information of hurricanes long before they had reached inhabited coastal areas. The planes, piloted by military and naval pilots during the war, established the system and the instant a developing storm came to any observer's attention, a plane took off to pinpoint the disturbance and measure its intensity.

By 1943 radar was in use and today the hurricane service has a network of these instruments along the Atlantic and Gulf coasts of the United States. In addition, many stations in the Caribbean have the sets which extend the horizons of observation.

Today with camera-bearing rockets and, more importantly, camera-bearing weather satellites, the skywatchers' vision extends over the entire globe. Hurricanes far at sea, undetectable by any instrument on distant coasts, are photographed in their entirety by the circling camera far above the earth.

In 1956 intensive research began into the nature and structure of hurricanes. It continues and although meteorologists have not yet analyzed all the forces and factors that build a hurricane, they hope eventually to understand these great storms in every detail.

Agricultural Service

Far less dramatic than hurricane watching is the Weather Bureau's continuing assistance to farmers throughout the country. Nonetheless, it saves millions of dollars annually. Next to flood and storm warnings, forewarning farmers of severe weather ahead is the oldest special service of the Bureau. The need for such information, in fact, was recognized before the Signal Corps began a weather service in 1871. In the 1840s, Pennsylvania appropriated funds to gather climatological data within its borders for the specific use of farmers. When the first forecasts came from Washington and were sent out over the telegraph circuits they contained warnings of cold fronts approaching large midwestern and southern areas. But it became evident that a central office, with the scanty data at hand, could not be specific enough to benefit individual farmers over a wide area. In short, a bulletin warning of lower temperatures over a three state area within the next few days, didn't tell the farmer on a particular piece of ground when the frost might strike, what night and how severely in his neighborhood.

The result often was that either the farmer spent a lot of time taking precautions that proved unnecessary or, becoming tired of so much wasted effort, did nothing and so got caught in a freeze. The need for decentralization was quickly apparent. During the Signal Corps reign, Cleveland Abbe and Major H. H. C. Dunwoody devised a plan of collaboration with various states. In 1878 Iowa passed legislation which assured that state's cooperation in what later became a national plan. Soon other states joined and in ten states, mostly midwestern, a corps of 2000 state-employed observers collected and reported data over and above the observations of the Weather Service men themselves.

At that early date in Weather Service history, the Signal Corps gave cold wave, frost and storm warnings to cotton, rice, corn and wheat growers and the information saved many a crop. In the areas where special climatological conditions and soil produce particular crops, the Weather Bureau has long given special attention. Fruit growers in California, Arizona and Florida get news of approaching low temperatures and when the forecast calls for a drop below 40°F in those sections, the orchards can be protected from frost with smudge pots. Elsewhere cranberry bogs can be flooded and tobacco can be harvested a trifle early to escape complete destruction.

By 1922 special fruit-frost reports went regularly to growers in the Pacific states, Arizona, New Mexico, New Jersey, the New England States, Wisconsin, Missouri, Illinois and Kansas.

So detailed is this work that Weather Bureau thermometers are actually installed in the orchards themselves. From studies of past records, the surface temperature—which may be slightly different from normal station temperature readings—could be checked and reported. In one instance in Florida the crop was largely saved when a two-day warning of a severe frost enabled pickers to harvest the citrus crop in time.

Today farmers can study the extended forecasts issued for their particular locality by Washington and know with reasonable accuracy what lies ahead. The accuracy of these forecasts increases as the science of meteorology advances. And farmers the country over, like those in Caribou, worrying about their potato crop, have only to snap on their radios or read the *Weekly Weather and Crop Bulletins* to learn what weather lies immediately ahead.

Severe Storm Forecasts

The midwestern section of the United States, from the Gulf States to the Great Lakes, is the most tornado struck spot on earth. So frequent are occurrences of this type of storm in these states that skywatchers term the area, Tornado Alley. The meteorologists' interest in tornadoes dates back in the United States more than a century. In 1841 James Espy deduced that tornadoes came from clouds whose formation went to great altitudes above the earth. Elias Loomis was among the first to note the explosive effect of these storms as they passed over buildings, from which he correctly reasoned that a great drop in atmospheric pressure at the vortex of the storm must exist for this to occur. But upper-atmospheric studies were lacking and the sporadic attacks of tornadoes did not allow the earliest skywatchers to proceed with any orderly analysis of these storms. Nonetheless, the Signal Corps, while administering the weather service in 1884, tried to forecast tornadoes. The effort aimed primarily at research and the man behind the scheme, Lieutenant J. P. Finley, worked hard to interpret weather data to predict the storms. Considering the handicaps under which he labored, Finley was reasonably accurate, but the forecasts he developed were not made public. The nearest approach to a warning was the issuance of bulletins which spoke of the possibility of severe local storms, or intense thunderstorm activity, in the affected area. Chief reason for secrecy was the fear that the straightforward statement, tornadoes may strike such and such a town today, would cause widespread panic. Few words in English can induce unreasoning fear as swiftly as the word tornado. In these storms, those who have survived, know there are forces of destruction that rival any in the storehouse of nature.

To this day the problem of advising the public of the possible occurrence of tornadoes poses problems. As the population of the midwestern area grew, the number of tornadoes striking towns, cities, villages and farms naturally increased proportionately. Many midwesterners felt that the number of storms was increasing year by year but the truth of the matter was that more men were getting in the way of the tornadoes than ever before. Whichever way the Bureau tried to forecast warnings, complaints came in. In 1896, for example, in St. Louis, forecasters recognized that tornadoes might well strike that heavily populated area. The soft-pedal approach was in favor at the time and on May 27, the Bureau warned that conditions were favorable for severe local storms or thunderstorms. The newspapers failed to take the hint and carried the previous evening's forecast of merely local thunderstorms. On that day a tornado struck St. Louis and killed a hundred people, passed into East St. Louis and exacted nearly the same toll of lives there. On March 18, 1925, a series of tornadoes swept three states all on a single day and the toll of lives reached 957. In one village, Parrish, Illinois, of the five hundred inhabitants, only three were left uninjured.

Severe local storms was the phrase used by the Bureau to say tornado without mentioning the dread word. Only in recent years has this policy changed. Today if conditions are favorable for the appearance of tornadoes, the Bureau will announce the fact and designate the general area that may be affected. Even so, people still write to newspapers and their congressmen and the Bureau complaining of the "useless trouble" to which people are put because of such bulletins. Unquestionably most of the complaining citizens have never witnessed a destructive tornado.

The conditions that must exist in the atmosphere for tornadoes to appear are only now being fathomed in detail. Briefly, the unstable conditions existing at the boundary of large masses of hot, moist air and cold, relatively dry air can cause tornadoes. This boundary, or squall line as it is often called, usually stretches over several states. Just where along this turbulent line tornadoes will form is a matter of conjecture but when the turbulence reaches a certain intensity high above the earth (where, by the way, it is difficult to obtain immediate, direct measurements) the funnel clouds can appear.

So important has this phase of forecasting become that a special Severe Local Storm Forecast Center has been established in Kansas City, Missouri, to keep track of the special conditions that can produce these storms. The observers in SELS, as it is termed, are in touch by teletypewriter and telephone with all other Bureau stations to give quick forewarning when the tornado experts spot a danger area.

The history of this special department of the Bureau is recent. World War II found many war-production plants and Army Air Bases mushrooming on the midwestern plains. So often did tornadoes damage these plants and fields, interrupting the production and training programs, that the Bureau, in cooperation with the military services, began to try a new approach to tornado warning. The storms are local and not long-lived. Their destructive swath is relatively narrow, measured in hundreds of yards, and their paths only a few miles long. When one forms, it moves on a town at about 40 miles per hour on the average and it is only that town or airfield that need be alerted. Calling on citizens during the war years, the Bureau built networks of volunteer observers who phoned to a Bureau or airfield station when a funnel cloud was sighted. Then, using radio and telephone, officials alerted towns or factories in the storm's path. So successful was this method that after the war the Bureau continued to use it in the most storm-struck regions.

An outstanding example of successful warning of tornadoes

is the case history of one which struck Fargo, North Dakota, on June 20, 1957. The area had been alerted to the possibility of tornadoes and then the phone rang in the Bureau station at the local airport. An alert citizen twenty miles from Fargo reported that a funnel cloud was visible near his location and that it had already touched the ground—he added that it appeared to be headed toward Fargo. Within minutes, another call reported the tornado nearer that town. The Bureau observer wasted no time. He phoned local radio and television stations telling them of the approach of the storm. Many people got into their cars and drove away from the storm (a sensible thing to do if there is time and the roads don't become jammed with traffic) but those who remained went to their basements and stayed in the southwest corner of the cellar. Since most tornadoes travel from southwest to northeast, this is the most protected spot in a home. The tornado approaching Fargo, however, was moving almost directly east. By the time it struck, most of the town's populace had been alerted and although great damage was done to property only eleven people lost their lives.

The Severe Storm Center in Kansas City does more than keep an eye on tornado conditions. As its name implies, severe storms are its province and blizzards and suddenly approaching cold waves qualify for the Center's attention. Normal cold-front activity, of course, is a daily ingredient of the weather map but the suddenness of some temperature drops puts them in the category of being disastrous to human life. Ranchers far from shelter—and cattle, too, for that matter—have been caught in sudden temperature drops and found frozen to death the next day. The most severe sudden temperature drop on record is extreme enough to make any skeptical critic pause to reconsider. During a twenty-four hour period, one January day, in Browning, Montana, the temperature plummeted from a relatively warm 44°F to minus 56°F—a change of 100°. Blizzards, too, sweeping in on an area can cause disaster. The suddenness and intensity of such storms can catch people in exposed places and seal their fate within minutes. In Silver Lake, Colorado, for example, seventy-six inches of snow fell during a single twenty-four hour period. All these sudden, intense weather changes are monitored by the Severe Storm Center and while any Bureau observer in any station can sound an alert for a storm, the Severe Storm Center is primarily responsible.

River and Flood Service

Forewarning of floods on the great and small river systems of the United States is a special task belonging to the Weather Bureau. Even people in localities where floods occur do not realize the frequency with which floods endanger life and property. Throughout the United States during a fourteen-year period, Bureau records show that floods occurred somewhere in the country in all but fifteen of those months. Summer, winter, spring or fall will bring inundation to some section of the United States.

Earliest methods of flood forecasting relied heavily on crude forms of river gauges strapped to bridge pilings. These instruments gave observers some indication of the threatening rise of the river but only after it had begun. As early as 1873 weather service observers sent daily reports of river heights to Washington where, if conditions called for it, a warning was issued by telegraph to the threatened area. Later, self-recording gauges were developed but the principle of forecasting remained the same: check the height and, where possible, the rate of flow of the river and issue the necessary warning.

In flood work, as in many of its efforts to serve the public, the Bureau was hampered by insufficient funds. Despite warnings from top meteorologists that the network of reporting stations was inadequate and poorly equipped, Congress and communities would wait until a serious flood caused death and destruction before money came to remedy the situation. Such a flood (accurately forecast by the Bureau) occurred on the lower Mississippi River in the spring of 1897 and in St. Louis in 1903. With these and other floods to focus on, the public grew alarmed and angry. Some people claimed that deforestation of the midwestern hills was causing more floods, but the Bureau maintained that the frequency of floods was not increasing. The fact which many people forgot to notice was that, as in the case of tornadoes, more people were living where the disasters struck than ever before. Although people were aroused, Congress wasn't, and the inadequate flood-warning network had to continue to operate as best it could. In their efforts Bureau men were helped by volunteer observers in many communities on the banks of the large rivers. These groups had, in fact, been in existence for many years. Citizens of Chattanooga, Tennessee, were the first to set up a river-warning system in 1881. Pittsburgh and St. Louis quickly followed. Some help came to the Bureau from the U.S. Geological Survey and the Corps of Engineers in the problems presented by rivers.

Gradually the old method of flood forecasting, the direct measurement of river heights, gave way to a new one: measuring precipitation in the headwaters of the river systems. This, plus such other factors as snowfall the previous winter, depth of frost penetration, amount of moisture in the soil and rate of thaw combined to allow the Bureau to forewarn of floods weeks and sometimes months in advance. In some areas where flash floods at the headwaters of small river systems caused damage, a closer watch was kept on precipitation rates. In western states in particular, the sudden fall of rain exceeds the soil's capacity to absorb it and great runoff swells the rivers very quickly.

The Weather Bureau river and flood forecasting services with headquarters in Washington, is subdivided into eleven river forecast centers which advise some eighty-nine river district offices. Today volunteer observers—reporting river stages and precipitation amounts—plus weathermen in the river warning system serve nearly 1600 localities where floods are most common. An outstanding example of early forecasting comes from the records of 1927. Great floods struck the Mississippi River and Mr. Isaac Cline of the New Orleans station and his assistant, Willard McDonald, gave early forecasts that enabled engineers to raise levee heights and save the city of New Orleans from serious damage by flood waters. An almost perfect example of forecasting comes from the efforts of the skywatchers on the Missouri River basin before and during the great flood of 1952. With their eye on the low temperatures and heavy snowfall of the preceding winter, the Bureau men forewarned of floods in the spring. Early spring temperatures remained low and then a sudden thaw in the headwaters of the Missouri far to the north and west of the cities and towns that would be affected, brought further warnings. As predicted, the waters swept down to the lower reaches of the river and raised its height eleven feet above flood level. Of course, some damage was unavoidable, but without the warnings, millions of dollars more damage would have been caused.

Fire Weather Service

On the forested slopes of mountains in the western states, one of the greatest natural catastrophes that can occur is a forest fire. The nation is rarely aroused by these events but when one occurs near a large city, the press of the nation gives it full coverage. Such a fire raged in the fall of 1961 near the homes of glamorous movie people and the newspapers reported it in lengthy columns. To lumbermen, to conservationists and Forest Service personnel the threat of loss of a vast natural resource such as timber needs no glamour to keep it uppermost in their minds. In the Southern California fire of 1961, only mesquite, manzanita and some scrub oak were burned. In the northwestern states great stands of fir with millions of board feet of lumber may go up in flames. As early as 1914 the efforts of the Weather Bureau were called for in predicting unusually dry atmospheric conditions over these areas. In 1926 a joint meeting of lumbermen, Forest Rangers and Weather Bureau men occurred in Oregon to develop the best plan of forewarning. The Weather Bureau had the data on atmospheric conditions and the amount of precipitation over a danger area for the past weeks and months. The Forest Rangers manned the lookout stations over national forest areas in the region and the lumbermen, of course, had their crews of men working constantly in the forests.

From this meeting came what the Bureau now calls its Fire Weather Service. Few summer tourists driving in the northwestern states, New England, or the Appalachian region have not seen the large signs along highways indicating the degree of danger from fire. In particularly bad seasons national forests may be closed to camping and all fire-building stopped. But while men start many of these fires, nature does its share, too. So-called dry thunder storms, where lightning strikes but no rain falls to dampen the parched earth, are the source of conflagrations. The Weather Bureau can forewarn of buildup of these great cloud igniters. Expanding from the use of two observers on a part-time basis in 1914, the Bureau now has thirty-seven reporting stations in critical areas.

Once a fire starts, the Bureau is still involved. As masses of heated air rise and as high- or low-pressure areas drift across the fire area, winds may shift suddenly. The Bureau keeps track of these capricious winds. To inform fire fighters, the Bureau now operates mobile weather stations. No major forest fire occurs without the dispatching of such a mobile station to the scene. There, an experienced meteorologist can predict the wind situation and advise the fire fighters who may shift their plan of attack as a result of the advice. The mobile station is in touch with the nearest Bureau station by radio and is thus in contact with the entire reporting network of stations which can give the mobile skywatcher a continuous flow of data.

In return for the help, the Forest Service stations, the lookout towers manned by the Rangers, have a set of weather-observing instruments and the Rangers regularly send data to Bureau Stations regarding wind, precipitation, temperature and humidity as well as a new yardstick called the forest fuel moisture content. This is measured with especially dried sticks of known weight which alters as they absorb moisture. These facts are

reported three times daily to the special fire-watch Bureau stations.

Climatological Services

Climate is long-range weather. But the data for this study
comes from each daily observation added to the preceding one
until a record of many years has grown in the files. From this
data climatologists can define the various climatic zones, specify the average rainfall and temperature and give the public
information that is in increasing demand.

Among the important factors that determine the location of
million-dollar businesses is climate: rainfall, water supply and
heating costs if the temperature is low. Climatic zones fix the
growing areas for certain crops; they determine the design of
buildings and in many cases the type of industry that can
thrive in an area. An outstanding example of the importance
of climate is the location of much of the United States aircraft production industry in Southern California where flying
weather is good nearly the year round.

Long ago, meteorologists understood the importance of keeping data to study climate, and Cleveland Abbe with J. Warren
Smith did much to preserve and classify data from the growing
number of Bureau stations between 1895 and 1913. Following
that period, however, little was done to expand or publicize
the climatological material on hand. During the years the data
piled up without being properly analyzed. Much of it came
from Bureau stations but a similarly large part came from the
corps of volunteer observers who faithfully mailed material to
the central office in Washington every day from as many as
3000 points in the 1890s. So vast did the backlog of material be-

come that eventually funds had to be granted to file it properly using a punch-card system. The tabulating center originally located in New Orleans finally was moved to the National Weather Records Center in Asheville, N. C. Today in that subdivision of the Office of Climatology more than 300 million data cards are on file and the number is being increased by about 35,000,000 per year. Machine sorted, the cards can be located and the data analyzed by processing machines quickly to save days or weeks of work and get the desired information either to a researcher or into a bulletin for public distribution.

These bulletins include the *Weekly Weather and Crop Bulletin* published every Tuesday as well as monthly issues of *Climatological Data* and a *National Summary* which go out to individuals or business and professional groups.

The number of different types of requests for data is so vast, a separate volume would be necessary to list them. But the Bureau tries to answer all of them with pertinent data and summaries. Are winters getting warmer in Minnesota? Will there be a long dry autumn this year in Pennsylvania? How will the ragweed crop do this year? (Of special interest to hayfever sufferers.) Will rain cause floods on the Platte River this spring? All these and many more questions constantly swamp the Bureau. It patiently tries to answer them but in at least one area the Bureau long ago gave up. Before the turn of the century, the Chief of the Bureau, Willis Moore, stopped the practice of having his meteorologists answer questions from citizens about the most healthful climate for particular ills. The Bureau has many skills, but medical knowledge and medical prognostication are not among them.

CHAPTER 7

How Weather Changed History

THE METEOROLOGIST today in Caribou or Washington or Idle-wild is milleniums removed from the first skywatcher among emergent groups of primitive men. Yet curiously today's modern meteorologist still depends on his sight for information, just as early man did. He must see the clouds and understand what weather they will bring.

Many historians have explored the ways by which weather and climate have changed history. Some have traced the evolution of man as he retreated in the face of great glaciers or migrated to less arid, more fertile plains and valleys in his ceaseless quest for food. The titanic changes that the ice ages brought are still not totally accounted for—a shift of the earth's axis of rotation is one theory, an as yet unaccountable diminution of solar energy is another. But these changes almost certainly were caused by forces affecting and being applied by the solar system. They underline the earth's—and man's—total dependence on the sun as the giver of all life. Little wonder then that primitive men developed religious views regarding the sun, blessing its appearance and praying for its beneficent rays if they were withdrawn.

According to anthropologists, when man emerged from the steaming tropical jungles, he did so not from a spirit of adventure but from necessity. Climatic changes apparently came to the regions of his development and forced him to move along smartly before the changes—whether in the form of glaciers from the north or an encroaching aridity that shriveled all the plants and forests within his sight. During that time and in the many centuries between then and now, man's greatest scourge has been famine: it strikes today in the populous countries of Asia; it struck in ancient times and wiped out large groups of people the world over. As a result, men spread farther and farther over the face of the globe in their ceaseless search for food. Originally nomadic, men moved in small groups along the streams toward forests and away from treeless, arid regions. But once a well-stocked stream was found where fishing was good the year round and fruits and nuts and berries could be gathered, he settled down and moved no more—until forced to. Through the years during which a tribe lived in one place, the arts of agriculture were developed and man, though he proved the advantage of tilling soil and herding animals, laid himself open to destruction from the weather. A year or two of drought, killing plants and animals, would also kill man. For in settling down he'd lost the knack of roaming and had also reproduced himself to such an extent that the loss of crops spelled disaster even as it does today.

As civilizations rose among the river basins and along the seacoasts of the world, climatic changes elsewhere often brought invasion from famine-stricken nomads who were migrating in search of more hospitable lands. Lost in unrecorded time, such migrations cannot be shown to have been caused entirely by climatic changes but neither can it be disproved. In Egypt during the Nineteenth Dynasty, the people found themselves harassed by periodic invasions from nomads of the Lybian Desert. Simultaneously, Palestine was enduring invasions from roving Semitic bands; northern invaders struck the Aegean and even the settled farmers of the Po Valley in Italy were under attack from outsiders.

According to historian John L. Myers, these and later invasions of settled, fertile regions by nomads were caused by vast climatic changes. ". . . it almost seems," he writes, "as if we were confronted with large cosmic occurrences of which these regional migrations were local symptoms.

"I venture to suggest that this cosmic occurrence was the periodical drying up of the great belt of grassland and desert which runs from Cape Verde to the Altai; that this desiccation forced the nomad pastoral people of the steppe to strike outwards . . . and that the periods of quiescence which intervened were phases of more copious moisture."

The most recent uprooting of men in the United States occurred during the great dust-bowl migration from the middlewest during the 1930s.

Not all such shifts of population have been from disaster toward salvation. In the nineteenth century many families in the Midwest along the banks of the Missouri and Mississippi rivers wore out their land with primitive farming techniques and set out hopefully westward toward untouched land. Without knowing it, they were moving from a region with over thirty-five inches of rainfall per year into a more arid area where rainfall of less than twenty inches demanded different farming techniques. In the years following these migrations, many families came to grief.

History is full of such fateful movements. One of the most important from America's viewpoint was the migration from Ireland to the United States in the 1840s. The great potato famine, as it was called, brought to our shores many emigrants seeking fertile lands or at least means of employment so they could avoid the spectre of famine. The vast miles of Russia have seen many such droughts and in the resulting famines millions have died. In China, during 1961, millions of Chinese met death by starvation when beneficent rains failed to come and the crops never ripened.

That these events have influenced history is not questionable. Intermingling of cultures, wars, great innovations such as irrigation and the development of more intelligent agricultural techniques, all combine to create the history of man throughout the world—and much of it is caused by the weather.

Individual cases where discovery or possession of new lands came as a result of weather are legion. Bermuda, for a small example, was discovered and became a British colony because a storm drove a ship's captain George Somers ashore on that hospitable island and allowed him to claim it for the English crown. Weather patterns now known to exist over the earth delayed the discovery of Australia, the opening of the northwest United States by sea, the discovery of Antarctica, and influenced the length of exploratory voyages of such historical stalwarts as Magellan and Diaz—limiting their discoveries and, in the case of Diaz, putting an end to all his effort in a storm at sea off the southern coast of Africa.

From the times of ancient Greece, men have recognized that weather can be the deciding factor in battles and wars. In those times, of course, a wise commander studied the local weather and selected what appeared to him to be the most favorable condition for his tactical move of the moment.

Unquestionably the most critical move in war in modern times which drew the attention of the world was the planned invasion of Europe in 1944 during World War II. General Eisenhower had under his command hundreds of thousands of allied troops. His mission was to carry out the largest amphibious invasion ever attempted.

The English channel, a notoriously boisterous stretch of water, had to be crossed. Prepared Nazi positions on the coast of France had to be struck at the right time by the combined forces of the air and sea as landing craft disgorged ground troops on the mined, wired and wave-strewn shores of Normandy.

Weather experts studied the patterns of weather from past records. They knew that much of it came to England and the Channel from far to the west, that it was influenced by Greenland with its huge icecap—a cold-wind generator of monstrous proportions—as well as by the confluence of the Gulf Stream and cold waters of the Arctic which mingle with warmer water near England's latitude producing dense fogs.

The decisions reached by the skywatchers were based on all the knowledge of the past that could be brought to bear. But even the most expert meteorologist in the world today can go wrong. Study of all the weather patterns in the past do not assure a worried commander such as General Eisenhower precisely and unequivocally what the weather will be in the future on specified dates.

Hence the meteorologists gave General Eisenhower and his staff sets of figures based on statistical analysis for the odds on certain weather conditions prevailing at various times. The decision, when it was taken, committed all those men and, as Mr. Churchill might have said, "all that treasure" of equipment to battle and nothing could have withdrawn them once they moved beyond a certain point.

What were the conditions that the various services wanted to carry out their missions? A list sounds fantastic but it was drawn up.

For the Navy, the minimum requirements were that there should be no continuous high winds for several days preceding the landing that would raise heavy swells in the Channel; that winds on the surface should not be above force 3 onshore or force 4 offshore in the proposed landing area from the time of landing forward for forty-eight hours. Winds could be boisterous enough, up to 27 miles per hour, for short times over the ocean but not for prolonged periods.

For the Air Force, there were several individual requirements for the various operations. Air transports needed 2500-foot ceilings along the way and over the target areas. The visibility had to be at least three miles. Heavy bombers needed a ceiling not less than 11,000 feet and no more than $5/10$ cloud cover below 5000 feet. Medium bombers had to have a minimum ceiling of 4500 feet and visibility over the target area of not under three miles. Fighters needed only a ceiling of 1000 feet. In England at the bases the weather required was a ceiling not below 1000 feet with visibility at least a mile. Heavy bombers needed a cloudless sky above 5000 feet with not more than a trace of lower clouds.

The chances of obtaining exactly what everyone wanted were extremely small. But meteorologists took the requirements and searched the past records of weather for seasons of the year when such conditions were most nearly matched by actual events. The months of May, June and July held out most hope. June offered the best odds and, since the allied commanders wanted the advantage of tides and moonlight during the late night hours before landing, this fixed the time areas within the first or third week of June.

General Eisenhower in concert with all of his advisers, chose the day of June 5th for the assault across the Channel. Long before this day or season approached, all the plans that men can make for a battle had been set in motion. But this was no ordinary invasion. Commanders from Alexander onward through history had faced tactical problems of varying size and complexity. But Overlord, as the World War II operation was named, was the largest, most complex invasion plan ever conceived by man. Five divisions of troops totaling 176,000 men plus 20,000 vehicles and all items of supply were to cross the Channel and begin the liberation of continental Europe. Eleven thousand airplanes were marshalled for the effort and the initial blow would involve 8000 of those. Units of the British and U.S. fleets from battleships to destroyers and transports would take part.

England became, in the words of Winston Churchill, "an armed camp." As the end of May approached, the camps in which the combat troops were marshalled were sealed off. Mail was delayed. Harbors and rivers were choked with landing craft and other vessels.

All that man could do was being done. But what about the weather? It became the question uppermost in the minds of Eisenhower and all the other allied commanders. Two meetings a day took place to consult with meteorologists and receive their briefing.

What were the winds aloft?

Were the expected pressure systems forming and moving at predictable rates?

What about clouds?

What were surface winds—winds that could kick up a sea in short order if strong enough?

Would onshore winds give an abnormal tide across the Channel?

The success or failure of the entire operation lay in the weather—in the great, shifting, indifferent patterns of air motion and energy in the sea of air surrounding the globe.

Anticipating trouble as shrewdly as possible the Allies drew up several alternative plans. If ships were not ordered out and landing craft not filled, adverse weather would simply mean further delay and increased risk of a security break. If the small craft were loaded and on their way and had to be recalled, there was even a plan for that. But a recall of any duration would be catastrophic. Battle-geared troops cannot be kept indefinitely in small, tossing landing craft. They have to go somewhere and get out—either on the enemy shore or on their own.

As June first approached, the weather took a turn for the worse. It became, as one Englishman put it, "More like December than June." The forecast then by weathermen was for low clouds on June 5th, D-Day. This would cancel all air operation and leave the entire invasion in a serious position if it were launched. By June 3rd, a westerly wind began to raise a great wave pattern in the Channel. The sky was overcast, gloomy, and the cloud base got lower and lower. But already, according to plan, ships began to steam out to sea to rendezvous points. The initial ponderous movements of the great organization had started and once begun appeared to be as unstoppable as "an avalanche."

Still the final decision was not made. General Eisenhower planned to wait until the last possible moment, which he decided was in the early hours of June 4th.

At 4:14 on that morning the weatherman brought the military men bad news. Strong southwesterly winds prevailed, the sky was still overcast and the clouds were low. It was raining. A moderate sea was running, whipped along by the surface winds. The forecast for D-Day called for even more adverse conditions.

General Eisenhower postponed the invasion. Messages went out to the steaming convoys at sea. The transports and destroyers, herding the thousands of small landing craft, signaled the landing craft commanders by blinker and the ships began turning back. One convoy failed to receive the message and hastily dispatched ships finally located it and turned it back.

Small craft ran for the coastal harbors and inlets. The larger craft, though crowded stayed at sea.

At 9:15 on the evening of June 4th, Eisenhower held another weather conference. He would either have to postpone for a longer period and send the men back to shore, or go ahead.

Weather conditions still were bad but the forecast now called for some improvement on the morning of June 6th. It would be, the weathermen warned, only a temporary improvement. After that, the weather would get considerably worse. The decision was to invade—subject only to a possible recall early on the morning of June 5th, 1944. But by 4:00 A.M. that fateful day the forecast remained as it had been: temporary improvement. The order went out and the five divisions and all the ships and planes were committed on the timetable of the weather.

Of this move, Churchill wrote, "In retrospect this decision rightly evokes admiration. It was amply justified by events, and was largely responsible for gaining us the precious advantage of surprise. We now know that the German meteorological officers informed their High Command that invasion on the 5th or 6th of June would not be possible owing to stormy weather, which might last for several days." *

The assault forces hit the beaches of Normandy on June 6th. To observers watching the awesome parade of naval craft it seemed as though nothing on earth could halt that massed might of the Allies. Five divisions were put ashore. Their supplies and vehicles followed. In England, ready to follow in the trail of the lead battle groups lay thirty more divisions. The schedule called for more than a million men to invade and liberate France and by twenty days after the first landing they all were supposed to be in France.

There was a force, however, which could turn the majestic scene of invasion into chaos very shortly. If the weather changed

* Quoted by permission of Houghton Mifflin Company, from *The Second World War* by Winston Churchill.

materially for the worse, the five divisions on solid ground could not be supported by those behind in England.

The weather did not improve but it did not turn bad enough to impede critically the plans that had been so long in the making. To the uninformed, it seemed even on D-Day that the "moderate seas" causing such distress among the landing craft and the lowering clouds that made the mission of the Air Force difficult proved that someone had misjudged the situation. Headlines in several U. S. papers spoke of a weather failure. But the men who wrote those words did not know that the forecast was precise and correct—and that had the invasion been postponed until the next possible conjunction of tide and moon, the worst weather for that period in twenty years would have caused untold loss of life and possibly have wrecked the operation at the outset.

As a matter of fact, the weather on June 6th was so marginal for the operation that not only was surprise achieved at the points of landing, but farther to the east Luftwaffe planes could not get off the ground to help repel the Allies—because of bad weather.

History tends to highlight certain events and perhaps no greater light is thrown on any of man's activities than war and battle. For in such engagements, the business of the historian becomes immensely simplified. This commander won a battle and changed the course of history, this admiral or general lost a battle and so a watershed can be discerned from which the course of events flow measurably and rationally beneath the historian's pen.

Many battles have hinged on the course of the weather from

earliest recorded history—and in those early times the primitive weapons and vehicles of man were subject to the caprice of weather so obviously as not to require explanation.

The arrow from a bow is deflected by the wind and the archer misses his mark. A wind, then, could cripple the aim of battalions of archers and so bring defeat.

Unfavorable winds could do the same thing to the sailing craft of long ago. A great fleet under the Persian, Xerxes, was anchored off the coast of the Greek peninsula and an invasion plan was about to be put into effect when a violent storm came up. Some ship commanders beached their craft but more than one third of the huge armada was wrecked by the storm and with those wrecks went the hopes of the Persians.

Weather also played an important role in the ruin of the Spanish Armada. In flight before the British ships, the Spanish fleet was beaten enough to retreat but their power remained largely intact. However, in a storm off the Hebrides, many of the large warships were wrecked—and sea power, the backbone of Spain's might, was gone forever.

Even on land and in more modern times when guns had replaced bows and arrows, weather has called the turn. One of the important factors in Napoleon's defeat at Waterloo was the unexpected rainfall the night before what was to have been a surprise dawn attack. With fields and roads heavy with mud, artillery and cavalry could not move swiftly enough. Dawn came and went. It was noon before the advance got under way and by that time all the element of surprise had vanished.

Weather, of course, can prove beneficial as well as troublesome. In one instance, during the American Revolution a sudden lowering of the temperature turned muddy impassable roads into perfect highways by freezing so Washington could maneuver his artillery and complete his battle plans.

With the nineteenth century, man began to feel the effects of weather during war more severely than before and governments began to take serious note of the weather factor in all planning. It might seem that with the growth of technology and science that men would design weapons and means of locomotion that reduced the factor of weather in military planning and action. Such, however, is not the case. The reverse is maddeningly true. Each advance in military technology has left man more rather than less at the mercy of the elements. To moralists, such chastisement as the weather inflicts on men at war might appear to be a hint of divine displeasure. But moralists do not design military weapons nor direct the course of a nation's interests.

During the Crimean war, British field commanders were advised to act only with favorable weather conditions. This platitude was largely without value since no one in Britain knew what conditions would be encountered on the Crimean peninsula. As a matter of fact, the winter weather there was so severe it caused much suffering among the troops and supply ships that went out from Britain encountered storms that sank many of them. A storm in November sank an entire fleet of supply ships en route to Crimea and increased the already heavy burdens of the men who were not sufficiently clothed nor adequately fed.

Mobility and visibility are twin factors that can spell defeat or victory to an army and, despite all man's ingenuity at invention, these two military factors are still largely controlled by weather. With the advent of the airplane, the possible extension of military vision became a reality—yet weather dominated the dimension in which planes operate. No longer was it enough to worry about weather on the surface of the earth, man had to plumb the air ocean above him to see if it would allow his planes to fly.

First used as a reconnaissance means, planes soon became weapons in their own right and until the advent of missiles were considered the major striking force of any power.

Well, what of missiles? Can't they ignore the weather? Not at all. Spanning thousands of miles in their flight, rising to the upper limits of the atmosphere, they run into winds aloft measuring as much as 300 miles per hour—and stay in those winds a sufficient time to be deflected from their target.

Visibility in more local engagements might be said to be insured by the advent of radar. Yet even here weather can confuse the picture. Extreme electrical disturbance of the atmosphere—either produced by particles sent earthward from the sun or due to local turbulence of air—can inhibit the all-seeing eye of radar.

Mobility of an army or a fleet still lies in the control of weather factors. In World War II in Italy, in Africa and in France muddy roads and low clouds stalled fighting tanks and planes. Less dramatic but equally as important as the fighting forces themselves are the vehicles of supply. A storm in the United States, delaying the loading and shipping of critical supplies, affected numerous engagements in Europe—and mud will stall a supply truck on the road to the front as quickly as it will bog down a tank.

Today all governments and all of their military arms have

meteorologists to maintain constant watch on the weather and produce forecasts as reliable as the science can make them with present methods and data. Every U. S. Air Force station has a weather section. Into it, from Weather Bureau stations and those of other Air Force stations, comes the endless stream of data that must be processed to give results.

As lately as World War II, however, the military arms of the United States encountered difficulty because of lack of knowledge of weather in certain areas of the world. The U. S. Navy operating in the Pacific Ocean areas suffered many times from the effects of unannounced and undetectable typhoons or hurricanes. Unless the planes of a Carrier Task Force accidentally encountered an approaching storm, the first indication to a Naval commander that he faced not only Japanese but also weather elements in a coming battle was the appearance of the typical low clouds and the rising winds of those intense, massive disturbances. Then if his planes were not back and safely lashed on deck, disruption of the military mission was almost unavoidable.

In England, the giant 8th Air Force, which struck daily at targets to the east in Germany, Czechoslovakia and Austria, had to keep a constant weather watch to the west over the trackless seas. For a flight east might be made in clear weather in the morning but impossible conditions could spring up by midafternoon as the bombers came homeward, low on gas, in desperate need of a place to land. To insure accurate information the Air Force sent daily weather flights to north, west and south of England to check conditions. Yet with all these efforts, the loss of planes due to weather exceeded those due to enemy action in the later phases of the war.

We are today being made aware of the increased dependence of man on the weather in the age of nuclear bombs. Should nuclear attack come to the United States, the question of who will survive and who will not is largely dependent on the errant winds. A recent survey of winds over prime industrial targets taken at the same instant revealed that if an attack had come at that moment, the people in southwestern areas would have experienced minimum fallout as would people on the northwest coast of the United States. The strongest winds which would send the radioactive dust along the farthest paths was occurring at that time in the midwestern region, and a map drawn up from that data showed the tracks of fatal fallout extended to the east and southeastern countryside surrounding such cities as Chicago, Kansas City and Minneapolis.

Studious analysis of local climates may assist some cities in planning protection against fallout in particular localities but few places in the United States do not have occasional winds from all points of the compass. Perhaps the only generality regarding the wind spreading radioactive particles is that since the general trend of air mass motion is from west to east, the eastern side of target areas is most dangerous.

Yet another factor enters into the problem. Although radioactive particles of various masses will fall out at proportionate rates (the heavier settling faster as might be expected), precipitation can occur that will change the pattern drastically. Rain, washing the particles from the atmosphere could put a higher concentration of radioactive dust on an area than otherwise would have fallen.

Such unknowable factors as altitude and strength of the exploding bomb or bombs add greatly to the problem. Estimates of the possible destruction to mankind show conclusively that it is possible that man may develop the nuclear weapon to such fantastic energy levels that pollution of the entire atmosphere of the globe becomes a real possibility. In 1885, when the volcano Krakatoa exploded, so much volcanic ash was discharged into the upper atmosphere that within a short time its presence was not only detectable by instruments, but was visible in every country of the world in the low and middle latitudes. Fortunately, man has not yet developed a single bomb that can approach Krakatoa's discharge of energy, but continued test explosions or the additive effect of numerous explosions detonated during a nuclear war conceivably could manage to pollute the ocean of air beyond the point of man's survival on the planet.

Skywatchers the world around are taking measurements of fallout as a regular part of their routine. In 1961 the Soviets' resumption of atmospheric testing raised the fallout rate in the northwestern and north central United States appreciably. Controlled U. S. tests in the atmosphere since then have been designed to avoid this.

Weather unquestionably has changed the course of history and we today may live to see it change that course once more— more drastically than ever in the past. For each step toward greater technological efficiency which man hopes will take him farther from dependence upon his natural habitat, will help him control it in fact, finds man face to face with unlooked-for greater dependence. We have the bombs. If mankind uses them, the winds of the world can wipe man from the earth—admittedly a drastic change of the course of human history. Yet these very winds may save him. Knowing that they will spread death all over the globe, man may have to bow before those natural forces and find a solution to his problems on a world-wide basis—surely as drastic a change in history's course as can be imagined.

CHAPTER 8

The Tomorrow of Skywatching

As WORLD WAR II acted to speed advancement in many fields of science, meteorology moved forward with large strides. Radar, designed to forewarn England and the United States of aerial attack, became a vital storm-tracking instrument. Improved direction-finding radio equipment followed the ascent of weather balloons. Jet aircraft development gave great impetus to commercial aviation and the demand for weather information for that industry alone soared to unprecedented heights. Following the formation of the United Nations, the former International Meteorological Organization became the World Meteorological Organization and the Weather Bureau's cooperation with other nations' efforts became part of daily operations. Weather was no longer a national business but an international one. Study of the air circulation in the northern hemisphere became real and meaningful as all nations agreed to exchange data. As soon as funds permitted, communication centers were linked around the world by teletypewriter and radio circuits. Early in 1961 the Bureau completed a long-desired link with Japan by means of a teletypewriter circuit from Honolulu to Tokyo. Today, the network girdles the globe with principal centers at

New York City, Frankfurt, Offenbach, Moscow, New Delhi and Tokyo.

Another outgrowth of the war was the involvement of the United States in Arctic regions. Aircraft flights over this area and its strategic importance brought meteorologists to Arctic stations in Thule, Greenland, where the United States cooperates with Denmark in manning a station. Other manned stations in cooperation with Canadian meteorologists include the northernmost Bureau outpost. The station, Alert, is on Ellesmere Island only 450 miles from the North Pole.

The war sent U.S. skywatchers literally to the four corners of the globe. During those years weathermen accompanied ground forces in all theaters of war and issued forecasts for local commanders. Africa, Europe, India and Southeast Asia, as well as the islands of the Pacific, became sites for the familiar whirling anemometer, the wind vane and the rain gauge of a weather station.

War censorship struck the Bureau, too. The west to east weather movement meant that Midwest conditions, if broadcast, could aid German submarines off the Atlantic Coast. California or Arizona weather forecasts could be picked up by raiders in the Gulf of Mexico. Consequently, during the first years of the war, a shroud of secrecy was drawn over weather information. Newspapers weren't permitted to picture weather maps. Radio announcers had to be very general in making remarks about the weather. The extremity of the situation was reached when announcers tried to tell baseball fans that the game had been called because of a situation familiar to everyone but which censorship prohibited reporting.

Where Arctic areas and weather became an immediate concern of the Bureau and military services immediately following the war, the Antarctic remained meteorologically unexplored. Then came the International Geophysical Year during 1956–1957. It put an end to weather ignorance of that continent for all time. While the Antarctic is remote from the United States, it does control much of the weather of the southern hemisphere —and U.S. meteorologists wanted to know about it. Today we have meteorologists permanently stationed at the South Pole and at several other stations on the continent.

Automatic Weather Stations

As the meteorologist reaches out to the more remote areas of the earth for a larger supply of data, he runs into two immensely practical problems. First is the question of cost. A fully staffed weather station in the United States, for example, costs about $60,000 per year to operate. Obviously this limits the number of stations the Bureau can create and stay within its budget. The other is that of recruiting men to operate stations in the remote areas of the world. The answer to both these problems appeared long ago to lie in some automatically recording and transmitting weather station. In a way, the small but efficient load of instruments carried aloft by balloons represents an automatic station. Temperature, humidity and pressure information can be sent by radio to receivers on the ground. But the batteries powering the transmitter have a short life. Long enough, of course, to last until the balloon finally bursts and the instruments are parachuted to earth—but not long enough to be placed in operation on the ground and left for any appreciable time.

The idea of automatic stations, despite technical difficulties

to be overcome, persisted. In 1954 the first such station went
into operation. Its data were transmitted by teletypewriter circuit automatically to the nearest manned station. Even this
advance contained the disadvantage of a limiting power source,
batteries which had to be replaced or recharged at regular intervals. A technician, it seemed, would have to make regular
rounds of such stations to keep them in operation and, of
course, instrument failure would demand even closer inspec-
tion and more frequent maintenance. One of the advantages,
however, of this type of recording and transmitting station is
that it can be installed on buoys at sea and thus bring in data
from areas never before covered. One such station gave accurate periodic reports on the advance of Hurricane Carla in 1961
and greatly helped the hurricane network in tracing the path
of the storm and measuring its intensity.

Skywatchers pin high hopes for the future of such stations
on the newest automatic device which uses atomic power instead of conventional batteries for a primary power source.

The first such station now is in operation on an uninhabited
island above the Arctic Circle in Canada's Norwegian Bay. It
lies between two manned Arctic stations which receive its data
by radio every three hours. The meteorological elements of the
station can measure and transmit temperature, pressure, wind
speed and direction within respectable limits of accuracy. The
radio transmitters have a range of 250 to 1500 miles depending
on the frequency used. But it is the power source that is unique.
Developed in conjunction with the Atomic Energy Commission, it consists of radioactive Strontium 90—the dreaded by-
product of nuclear explosions. Heat energy given off by the
radioactive fuel operates a special thermoelectric cell which

keeps a long-life battery charged with enough power to operate the transmitters—of which there are two operating on different frequencies.

One of the big problems solved in developing the atomic fuel cell was that of protecting nearby workers in servicing and transporting the station. Over 1600 pounds of lead in a stainless-steel case keep the radiation from workers. The material of which the strontium is a part, strontium titanate, cannot dissolve in water. Should the unit be inadvertently dropped or the atomic fuel exposed to the elements, it cannot contaminate either water or food grown in the nearby earth.

The entire station with its unique power source is about eight feet long. The large cylinder now is buried to a depth of five feet in the frozen ground of the Arctic. The station anemometer and thermometer are fixed to a nearby tower and the two antennas, 90 and 150 feet long, complete the automatic skywatcher. Extensive tests conducted before the station went into operation assured the Bureau that, barring great accidents, the station would continue to send messages every three hours, day and night, for at least two years before anyone would have to visit it again.

With this solution of the power source problem, research men in the Bureau and military services now are busy developing more equipment that can operate unattended, which will transmit such data as amount of sky cover, precipitation and perhaps even cloud types without the necessity of human observation.

Satellites

Despite the many manned and automatic stations around the

world which send data to the National Meteorological Center in Washington, many millions of square miles of the earth's surface and the atmosphere above it remain unobserved. In the Antarctic, for example, on a continent which is two-thirds the size of the entire North American continent, there are only a handful of observation stations. The great oceans of the world, particularly the Pacific and Indian oceans, are blank spots on the weather maps except for the transient reports from steamships and aircraft that pass over the watery surfaces.

Skywatchers long have dreamed of invading these areas by one means or another. Great numbers of automatic stations powered by atomic energy are one means of dotting the land masses with reporting centers but the difficulty of placing even these efficient items in remote areas is a handicap, and meteorologists cannot dot the seas of the world with floating stations. In any event, these stations would be able to report ground level conditions only. The vertical dimension of the atmosphere would remain unobserved.

With man-made satellites in orbit all this is changing rapidly. From the launching of the first successful satellite, meteorologists joined the throng of scientists from other fields of study who wanted to make research dreams come true.

Among the observations that skywatchers wanted to make—and knew would be attainable quickly with satellites—were photographs of cloud formations by means of television cameras. Such photographs of the top of the weather could unlock secrets that all efforts on the ground and up through the atmosphere had yet to reveal. Another important aim was to measure the amount of solar radiation on the blanket of air in which we are wrapped, as well as the amount reradiated by the earth which escapes into space. This incoming and outgoing energy, referred to as the "heat budget," affects all the winds of the earth, the movement of huge air masses and determines, in the long run, changes in climate that are now unmeasurable. With detailed continuous information of this heat budget, the meteorologist is in a position to make more accurate long-range forecasts and even may be able to anticipate and fore-warn of climatic changes that will affect the whole earth.

From the vantage point of a satellite circling the earth other important measurements may be made also. A constant watch can be kept on precipitation over the seas and uninhabited lands of the earth. With the use of infrared measurements, the skywatcher can receive information about the makeup of the atmosphere. This includes the water vapor held in the air, the amount of carbon dioxide and the ozone content of the air which absorbs great quantities of solar energy. With the satellite the meteorologist and other scientists can make more accurate measurements of the solar spectrum. Not least among the aims is that of measuring the amount of meteoric dust which falls into the atmosphere to determine whether or not this material from space helps seed clouds and causes precipitation.

If nothing more is accomplished than the photographing of clouds, the entire weather satellite program will be well worth the effort. Storms now develop over the oceans far from observation and they move sometimes erratically so that it is difficult for shore stations to track them. In 1954, for example, Hurricane Carol came nearly to a halt off the coast of the southeast United States and then during a single night picked up such forward speed that it reached Long Island sooner than expected. In many cases storms develop at sea and move rapidly toward the coasts. Although their tracks are generally predictable, no single storm will necessarily follow an average course. Sometimes hurricanes developing in the Atlantic just north of the equator follow a completely erratic route, turning south—which is most unusual—or even making a complete circle and striking the same area twice. In 1957 the German sailing ship, *Pamir,* was caught in the vortex of such an erratic storm and sunk with a loss of nearly eighty lives. Satellites, maintaining continuous surveillance of storms far at sea, will make all such catastrophes avoidable.

Still another important revelation that may come from satellites is the tracking of the jet streams—those rivers of high-speed wind which circle the earth. Their exact location and the determination of their seasonal shift can be a great help to high-flying commercial jets. Study of high cloud photographs from satellites will help do this, as will the use of infrared-detecting instruments that can spot temperature differences in the atmosphere. And between the jet streams and the surrounding air there lie distinct temperature demarcations.

The first weather satellite orbited the earth on April 1, 1960. Its name, Tiros I, comes from the key letters of the designation Television and Infrared Observation Satellite. This first satellite contained two television cameras. Its orbit was above the atmosphere and nearly circular. At apogee, its farthest distance from the earth, it was 461.3 miles above the surface. At perigee, its closest approach to earth, it was 436.0 miles overhead. Tiros I circled the earth once every 99.24 minutes and within three weeks after launching had completed about 300 trips, during which time it had sent to earth receivers nearly 6000 pictures of clouds. On its 125th orbit, Tiros photographed a fully developed storm 800 miles east of Brisbane, Australia, and Dr. Reichelderfer had the unique pleasure of notifying the head of the Australian Bureau about a storm heading his way which had not yet been observed by Australian shore stations.

"What this means," Dr. Reichelderfer announced at the time, "is that hurricanes spawned anywhere over vast oceanic areas can be detected much earlier than ever before possible. It also gives hopes that with future weather satellite camera systems man will be able to solve the tornado observation problem in the United States."

The planned life of Tiros I was about three months. During that time all the data was eagerly examined by skywatchers in Washington. The cloud pictures sent down fulfilled everyone's highest hopes. Storm centers were plainly visible as great disks of clouds with spiral arms trailing outward. By June, 1960, preliminary studies of the data were well under way and photographs of the cloud systems were dispatched to meteorological centers throughout the world. By the time Tiros I had stopped transmitting, over 20,000 pictures had been taken.

On November 23, 1960, Tiros II went into orbit. Weighing 280 pounds it carried, like Tiros I, two television cameras and, in addition, infrared sensors or measuring instruments. By the time photographs began coming from the second weather satellite, the ground observers and the entire global network of meteorologists had been alerted. With the emphasis still on research of the potentialities of such vehicles, the U. S. Weather Bureau in conjunction with the Air Weather Service, the Naval Weather Service, the Geophysics Research Directorate, Allied Research Associates, plus meteorologists from the Meteorological Satellite Laboratory sent teams to two stations, one in New Jersey and one in California, where the data sent down by the satellite would be received and processed. Within two hours after reception of photographs, a map reached the National Meteorological Center in Washington and nearby Navy and Air Weather centers. To keep meteorologists the world around informed, duplicate maps went out from NMC by radio facsimile as rapidly as possible.

Here then was worldwide use being made of data from a single satellite. The Weather Bureau in Washington had a cloud map of the satellite's track as rapidly as the organization could put it out and others interested in the data received it not too much later. By January, 1961, analyses from Tiros II were going to nearly 650 government, military and commercial stations in some 330 cities.

During its swing over the southern hemisphere, Tiros II took cloud pictures of weather south of Australia. These went to the International Antarctic Analysis Center in Melbourne, Australia, and aided the U.S. Navy resupply mission to the stations in the Antarctic by showing the weather over the sea route from Australia and New Zealand south to Antarctica.

To compare the satellite data with conventionally obtained data, many scientists cooperated.

At weather stations, like Caribou, personnel made a visual check of cloud conditions at moments when Tiros II was overhead. To check the presence of Tiros II the technician in Caribou had a special radio receiver tuned to Tiros' broadcast frequency.

Radar specialists sent in radar-screen pictures of cloud cover at the instant Tiros II was overhead.

Aircraft pilots reported weather conditions at the same time. Photo-reconnaissance planes operated by Air Force and Naval pilots made special flights. Cameras set up by the Geophysics Research Directorate of the Air Force took horizon-to-horizon cloud pictures as the one small space vehicle sped by above the cameras.

By the time Tiros II had stopped functioning, the Weather Bureau had learned much, not only about what a weather satellite could do, but also about how to process and spread the data quickly from ground stations. Tiros IV with a better camera than its predecessors, has produced even clearer, more comprehensive pictures, and today a group of analysis stations makes routine of what only a few years ago was nothing but a dream: an observation station in the sky.

Research

Most scientists enjoy work in a laboratory. A chemist can ask any question he wishes regarding his science and then attempt to find the answer among his test tubes and flasks and distillation apparatus. A physicist can isolate a problem and attack it with ingeniously designed equipment. Even oceanographers can build miniature seas, controlling the temperatures, salinity, and amount of organic life present as they seek the answer to a perplexing problem. But the meteorologist, save in very few cases, cannot. His laboratory is the sky. Specifically it is the entire atmosphere over the earth and the sun also—as well as some aspects of the space beyond the atmosphere.

To work in his laboratory, the meteorologist must have as many observers at as many various levels and at as many places on the earth as his money will allow. For him, the road to success in answering a host of questions lies in increasing the number of eyes turned on either the sky or the instruments that are scanning the sky electronically or photographically.

Top Bureau men see the entire problem naturally dividing into applied research and pure or theoretical research. As many uninformed Americans still question the value of pure research, the money spent in this direction must be defended vigorously. It is easy enough to see that taking ground-level temperature measurements in a fruit orchard as the frost season approaches will pay off with a saved crop. It is not so easy to see why, for example, money should be spent attempting to measure periodically the percentage of ozone in the atmosphere.

Meteorologists, like other scientists, are specialists and have developed a workable jargon for their science. This makes communication with even an interested layman difficult. On top of this lies the fact that most people, without the training, cannot follow the details of explanation and see the possible value in many areas of the research now being planned and undertaken by the Bureau. A picture from Tiros III, for example, is dramatic and convincing. What the cloud pattern means and how it can be effectively used is quite another matter.

Chief Reichelderfer, nonetheless, directs the Bureau today in an era during which research is expanding as never before in its history. New tools, new theories, more observation data and improved communications all help this immense expansion.

The problem is immense, too. Take two billion cubic miles of air. Heat part of it. Cool part of it. Put water vapor in some of it. Allow the water vapor to condense and fall as rain somewhere else in its mass. Let the colder parts of the mass mingle with the warmer. Pass some of it over a hot, dry land surface and then over open water. Then tell exactly what will happen all over the globe.

Chief among the problems the skywatchers are trying to solve is the fundamental one of the controlling weather factors. What are they? How do they stand in relation to each other? If these factors can be pinned down and their relationships discovered, then conceivably a formula or set of formulae can be constructed that will prove efficient enough to work. It is toward this one end that most pure research is directed.

To develop any equations at all, a scientist must know the items he is dealing with and must suspect or deduce a relationship between, say, pressure and temperature and water-vapor content and solar-radiation effects and a score of other items.

So far, in the laboratory that is the sky, the meteorologist has been fairly successful. But his success lies as much in the art as in the science of weather forecasting. The problem of the weather may thus seem to be incapable of mathematical solution. Yet that conclusion is farthest from the minds of meteorologists today who are boldly plunging into the maze of data, theories and weather phenomena. Here are several areas of investigation and the research projects in these areas:

Hurricane and Tornado Research

For years skywatchers have known general facts about hurricanes. But this knowledge is not sufficient to tell them what they want to know—not enough, for example, to tell them the three things that are most important to learn to protect the lives and property of U.S. citizens.

1) How to predict accurately the storm path and future intensity of such storms.

2) How to predict the maximum storm surges or abnormal high water on coastal areas affected.

3) How to collect and arrange *all* the factors that spawn, feed and move these destructive storms along their paths.

Since 1955 coordinated efforts of several government agencies under the administrative control of the Weather Bureau, plus special research projects being carried on in several universities, have been going on under the title of National Hurricane Research Project.

To collect data, newly equipped aircraft carrying the latest weather instruments penetrate the storms and improved radar focuses on them. With vast quantities of data coming in, such items as the distribution of temperatures throughout the storm, precipitation patterns, humidity patterns, wind variations and convective current studies, the problem of processing data has led the Miami headquarters of the NHRP to employ computers to digest and relate the information.

From the processed data on individual hurricanes, physical models are constructed and, for the first time, man has "built" a hurricane for his study. These studies go forward in universities such as Florida State, the University of Chicago and Massachusetts Institute of Technology.

When these little-heralded researchers find the relationships among enough factors measured in hurricanes, the forecasting and tracking of such disturbances will be more accurate. Separate studies aimed at accurately predicting high-water levels on coasts due to storm surges caused by hurricanes will allow the Bureau to forewarn inhabitants of danger areas in plenty of time and tell them where safety lies.

Tornado research at the Severe Local Storm Center in Kansas City has taken a direction similar to that of hurricanes. The Bureau has joined in this effort with the Federal Aviation Authority, the Air Force, the Navy and the National Aeronautics and Space Administration to analyze tornadoes, the most intense atmospheric disturbance that exists. As yet this joint effort has not developed precise equations to forecast the appearance of tornadoes. Today, during the tornado "season" in the Midwest and other less affected parts of the country, the Bureau forewarns the public in an area of about 10,000 square miles that there is likelihood of tornadoes when the conditions exist in the sky. Meanwhile, work goes forward on research. Promising leads have developed in the interpretation of radar pictures of storm-breeding clouds as well as the analysis of lightning intensity within the clouds themselves. Like their larger counterparts, hurricanes, tornadoes demand that men build physical models and probe deeper into the physics of their formation before they will give up their secrets.

Forecast Research

In addition to studies of abnormal disturbances of the atmosphere, the Bureau continues its inquiry into normal weather patterns with a view to increasing the accuracy of all forecasts. Studies on the effect of friction between moving air and the earth's surface irregularities indicate that a reduction in forecast error can be made. Energy studies of the atmosphere over the entire northern hemisphere will help eventually to make another meteorologist's dream come true: the forecasting of weather by using equations rather than relying on the skill of experienced forecasters. The Extended Forecast Section of the Bureau also wants accurate equations to work with to prepare its thirty-day outlooks. These aims and even more far ranging ones on climate may well be influenced by studies now being conducted at Massachusetts Institute of Technology on the relationship between variations in the amount of solar energy reaching the earth and the circulation of the atmosphere.

Fire Weather Research

Important weather factors in the development of "fire weather conditions," particularly in the western states, are local wind and relative humidity. Studies of these and other factors are carried on in Berkeley, California, in conjunction with the U.S. Forest Service. While a burning index has been developed which involves wind speed, relative humidity, fuel moisture and accumulated precipitation, work goes forward to develop a so-called ignition and risk index. Lightning, which starts many of the forest fires, also is being studied, particularly in thunderstorms which are termed "dry" since they carry little moisture to put out the fires which they start. At Missoula, Montana, with the Forest Service, the Bureau is examining not only the "dry thunderstorms," but the weather conditions that produce them, the electrical structure of the clouds and the probable number of lightning discharges.

Flood Research

Regular weather stations plus volunteer observers send data regularly to the flood prediction experts of the Bureau. Among the current projects are those studying evaporation of moisture from water surfaces, soil moisture content, rainfall frequency, effect of tropical storms on rainfall in the latitudes of the United States and guides for estimating probable maximum precipitation. Some of these projects already have yielded information that can be put to use in the country's River Forecast Centers. As new factors are tested and related, they will fit into the day-to-day mechanism of the Bureau which informs and alerts the public to possible danger.

Other Questions

As might be expected, anything that exists in the atmosphere is of interest to meteorologists and this interest has led them to participate in fallout and air-pollution studies. In many weather stations regular measurement is made of the amount of radioactive debris in the air and special, sensitive radar is being focused on such pollution problems as that of smog in Los Angeles and other industrial centers. Still another basic question is being studied. How do raindrops form? Meteorologists know in general what occurs with the condensation of water vapor on dust or other "particles" suspended in the atmosphere, but in laboratory and field stations more detailed answers are being sought. The meteorologist also is going farther up, to stratosphere levels, for studies there of everything he can find.

Changing the Weather

In times of drought, primitive man developed rituals, dances and incantations designed to bring rain to the parched earth. Shortly after World War II meteorologists began what they hoped was a more scientific method of producing rain: seeding clouds with dry ice, silver-iodide crystals or other particles on which the suspended vapor could condense to form raindrops. These studies marked the first serious attempt of skywatchers to modify weather. Newspapers during those first years of experiment carried dramatic accounts of the success or failure of the attempts. Cloud-seeding studies struck a responsive chord in editors who were aware that science was important but who rarely could find a way to humanize or dramatize the work. But here were modern rainmakers, here were men changing their environment by applying scientific knowledge—and here, everyone hoped, was the end of disastrous drought and of equally catastrophic precipitation causing floods. But here, in fact, men almost immediately ran into trouble. Some cloud-seeding efforts failed. Others succeeded. Sometimes clouds seeded in one area of the country drifted to others before releasing their moisture, and if the area where rain fell already had too much, lawsuits threatened.

There is little doubt that seeding does sometimes modify clouds and speed the rain-forming process. But since the rain probably would have fallen anyway, the value of the seeding becomes questionable. The World Meteorological Organization reported in a summary on weather control that "In our opinion, a net increase of precipitation has not been demonstrated beyond reasonable doubt in any seeding operations yet described in the scientific literature, and it seems that most of the claims made in other publications and in newspapers have not had adequate foundation."

What meteorologists lacked in this first assault on the weather was quite simply knowledge of all factors involved and their interrelationships. The WMO, in fact, stated in 1955 that "At least several years of fundamental investigations and of meticulously planned and analyzed seeding experiments will be needed before a reliable assessment of the economic potential of seeding operations can be made."

To keep the horse and cart in their proper places, in any attempt to modify weather, meteorologists know they must do the research and understand the entire mechanism of the atmosphere before they can intelligently approach the question of modification.

In the mid-nineteen fifties, when hurricane activity was intense along the Atlantic Coast of the United States, many people wrote the Weather Bureau asking why we didn't just set off a few thermonuclear bombs and break up the storms. The letters revealed an awesome lack of understanding about the forces of the atmosphere. Yet the Bureau responded to these letters and issued a report in 1956 discussing the question. Among other sound reasons for not rushing out with plane loads of bombs (ignoring the expense factor completely) the Bureau stated that it could not determine whether such explosions would break up the storm or merely intensify it. If such explosions intensified the storm, the exact reverse of what was wanted would occur. It is this great unknown effect of weather modification attempts that gives meteorologists pause. "We must know more," they say. In the realm of normal weather, this statement holds true. In a discussion of modification problems and plans, Chief Reichelderfer has said, "We must first explain why the atmosphere behaves the way it does. . . . Until we are able to do this, we will never be able to tell what weather control would bring forth. It could lead to worse weather rather than to improved conditions."

Several reflective observers have wondered whether we actually should tamper with the giant forces that control the atmosphere—whether we might not be better off by learning to live with nature rather than conquer it. To this proposal one realistic meteorologist has said, "Whether man should try to control the weather or not is beside the point. If he can, he will."

To date, however, meteorologists have had little success in actual modification attempts. The fundamental investigations are still going on.

Yet when man does find the answers to his questions about the weather, he raises a great many other ones which have little to do with science. No one doubts that it would be a good thing to make arid lands productive; divert or break up destructive storms, prevent flooding and regulate the amount of precipitation falling on farmlands. But if the knowledge being sought is misused, weather can be a weapon in the hands of an enemy. If an unfriendly power possessed it, which they unquestionably would, that power could deny rain to the farmlands of its enemies, it could turn countries into deserts or produce excessive precipitation causing paralyzing floods. Like atomic energy, weather modification has its negative as well as its positive value.

CHAPTER 9

Professionals and Amateurs

As IN ANY other profession, men who have chosen meteorology come literally in all shapes and sizes and from different backgrounds. There is no single distinguishing characteristic, save perhaps a long-range interest in science. From the Bureau Chief down to the newest recruit on the Bureau's payroll, all skywatchers have exhibited a strong curiosity about the weather. Where did they find this interest? How are they trained? How do they view their work?

In the earliest days of the Bureau's history, many observers were induced to undertake the endless chores of instrument reading on the basis of making a living wage—or supplementing that gained in some other work. Thus under early leadership telegraphers doubled as observers. At the turn of the century only a few men were scientifically trained to cope with the growing body of knowledge that today forms the science of meteorology. For meteorology is a young science. Although man has speculated on the causes of weather for thousands of years he has only recently tackled the job of understanding the weather with the money and skill necessary for success. Early meteorologists were all trained in some other science with a strong foundation in physics. For one reason or another they found themselves involved with weather observation and fore-casting and continued in the study of the growing science.

While it is impossible to say accurately what draws men to a lifelong study of weather, it is likely that awareness of the awesome forces of the atmosphere, plus a perhaps disguised appreciation of the beauty of the sky in all its moods, played their parts in the decision to follow the weather and the science wherever it led them. To some, of course, it is merely a job that pays for bread—which is true of many men in other profes-sions. To some it is a challenge to conquer, by joint effort with his fellows, the monstrous storms that loom each year from the Gulf and Caribbean areas, or the tornadoes that ravage the Midwest. To others, it is the keen delight experienced in suc-cessful research, the unlocking of one more secret of nature, revealing it to fuller understanding by them and, eventually, by everyone. To still others, the endless game of forecasting accurately represents a challenge that never ceases to delight and exasperate them to more careful study, more faithful ob-servance of the myriad rules, known or suspected, by which weather forms and moves across the earth.

Prior to World War II, the Bureau and the science of mete-orology were relatively small operations. Spurred by the de-mands of that global conflict meteorology grew into a major science with both theoretical and applied branches. Hundreds of meteorologists were needed for the war effort. To meet the demand, experienced meteorologists from the Bureau began training military skywatchers as fast as possible. These in turn trained more men. The demand did not end with the conclu-sion of the war. The commitments of the United States all over the globe demanded surveyed air routes, air routes along which weather was reported constantly.

Many middle-aged skywatchers today received their training in the armed services; many younger ones learned their special trade there, too, in the postwar years. In fact, a great number of stations scattered throughout the United States are presently manned by personnel, 80 or 90 per cent of whom are service trained.

Prior to World War II, few universities granted a degree in meteorology and many present meteorologists received education in physics or some allied field and later became meteorologists when experience with the Bureau fitted them for that designation.

The two general goals these men work toward are being in charge of stations or areas and leading a research project. In other words, rising to professional eminence through the working weather stations or through successful completion of difficult and valuable research projects.

The men working in the weather stations of whatever size have a wide choice of type and location of station. From above the Arctic Circle to the South Pole itself, from an isolated Pacific Island to the large urban station in New York City's RCA building, there are stations to be manned. Openings in various areas and in various job categories are regularly displayed on station bulletin boards. When a young weatherman has studied sufficiently and developed enough skill for a higher rating and a more responsible job, he often applies for transfer to another station needing the higher rating to complete its staff. But there is the challenge of adventure in many of the distant and different assignments. Family men, naturally, are more cautious about acceptance of higher ratings in primitive environments.

The meteorologist in charge of a station is designated as just that: Meteorologist in Charge or MIC, as the abbreviation becomes. While much of his time is spent in administration, he will, as Mr. Hattman does in the small station in Caribou, Maine, take an active part in the assessment of information and the forecasting of the weather for the area.

The path of research may lead a Bureau man to join a special project group made up of Navy and Air Force meteorologists like the one that started the Joint Numerical Weather Prediction Unit. Research may send a meteorologist to a university where, in laboratory experiments, basic weather equations and theories are developed and tested. A reasearch man may spend years becoming an expert on certain phases of meteorology such as climatology, storm analysis and prediction, storm surges along coastlines or some other field.

All Bureau personnel are under Civil Service and their pay and advancement conform to the rules of that government system.

The need for college-trained meteorologists is rising year by year. Recognizing this, the Bureau in 1956 began a unique program directed at high-school graduates who were interested in science. A summer student-training program was inaugurated with 25 students. All the selected young men were doing undergraduate work in science or mathematics in an accredited college or university. The Bureau offered them summer employment at one of the hundreds of Bureau stations across the country. Salaries today range from $67.00 to $77.00 per week, depending upon the number of years of college the student trainee has completed. During the first year or two of college, the selected students usually work in regular Bureau stations near their homes. Those in the later years of undergraduate study may be assigned to more distant stations where a different meteorological program is being carried out.

Four years after its inception the program involved 120 students, most of whom were majoring in meteorology. Some are mathematics students, some are physics majors but all are working toward a degree that the Bureau knows it can use in the expanding business of skywatching.

During the summer of 1960, for example, students across the country were involved with the daily routines of a surface-weather observation station, airport stations where they practiced pilot briefing and learned all the observational techniques, fire-weather stations, severe local storms projects, river and flood control projects and stratospheric analysis projects. One student trainee, a mathematician, wrote of his acceptance as a trainee: "It came as a surprise when I discovered last spring that the Weather Bureau was looking for mathematicians for its student trainee program. What I had forgotten was that meteorology, like any exact science, requires research and that research is extremely limited without several people who know a good deal of mathematics."

In reports requested by the Bureau from other students, all mentioned the value of the program and their growing interest in the profession. These embryonic skywatchers are, in fact, receiving the very best kind of education: theory during the winter and on the job application all summer. One young man had been a volunteer observer for the Bureau during his high-school years. He chose meteorology as his college major and then discovered, to his delight, that he could earn and learn at the same time. The trainee program draws top-ranking students from the entire country. An interested student can obtain an application blank either at his local post office or college placement office. Written inquiries should be addressed to Chief, U. S. Weather Bureau, Washington 25, D. C., Attention: Personnel Management Division.

Selection is made from lists of eligible applicants prepared by the U. S. Civil Service Commission. A student's acceptance depends upon his academic background and special test results.

High-school students interested in meteorology as a career can begin preparing for the trainee program before graduation by becoming a cooperative unpaid observer, setting up his own weather station (see p. 150) and taking all the science and mathematics courses available to him.

The number of colleges offering a degree in meteorology is growing and today includes: University of California, University of Chicago, Florida State, University of Hawaii, University of Michigan, City College of New York, New York University, University of Oklahoma, Oregon State University, Pennsylvania State University, San Jose State College, St. Louis University, Texas A & M, University of Texas, University of Utah, University of Washington, University of Wisconsin.

Some colleges offer courses in meteorology but no degrees in the subject. They are University of Arizona, Colorado State University, Johns Hopkins University, Oklahoma State University.

Massachusetts Institute of Technology and Columbia University offer graduate degrees in meteorology.

Rutgers University offers a degree in climatology and both

Pennsylvania State College and Oregon State College offer meteorological courses through their correspondence schools.

The list of universities offering work for budding skywatchers is growing and undoubtedly more will be added to the above lists. As of this writing the University of Nevada is joining the ranks by developing a meteorology curriculum.

Many of today's professional meteorologists developed their interest in the science when they were quite young. In high school or before, they began to read articles and books on the subject and then they took the next logical step: setting up their own weather station.

Many people who developed this interest in skywatching, of course, did not enter the profession but a surprising number have continued in their adult years to watch the sky and to read their collection of instruments while making their best attempts to forecast the weather for friends and neighbors. No estimate can be made of all the people today who are skywatching hobbyists but there are thousands in cities, towns and in rural areas who carry on regular observations with more or less elaborate equipment.

The advantage to men and women on farms or in some other occupation whose operation depends on the weather is obvious. But the practical benefits to a stockbroker, a banker or a plumber are few, and at first glance it may be difficult to justify their interest in observing the weather. Yet stamp collecting, bird watching or model boat building do not necessarily have to be of practical importance to engage and hold the interest of the hobbyist. The activity for its own sake brings its own rewards. Any good hobby is rejuvenative and recreational. Skywatching is both of these and much more.

Among many other benefits are:

Increasing respect for the problems of scientific measurement.

Understanding of the meaning of science and what it can and cannot do.

Growing awareness of the natural elements so often taken for granted.

Appreciating the very real beauties of the sky that escape notice by busy people.

Perhaps the most overlooked advantage of this hobby is that anyone can practice it anywhere. Whether the hobbyist lives in an expensive apartment in a crowded city, a modest house in the suburbs or in the most remote rural area, he lives twenty-four hours a day within the weather. With a very modest expenditure and some ingenuity he can build or purchase instruments he needs to begin his observations. Depending on his desire, he can read as deeply into the subject as he wishes for most libraries have books from elementary to advanced levels of meteorological instruction. As the record of his observations grows, he can begin to make relatively accurate one-station forecasts. With a continuous record to refer to he can tell quickly whether present conditions are normal for the season and the time of day and he also can relate the present trend of conditions to a similar situation in the past.

Weather Observation Instruments

Equipment for a weather observation station can be either quite simple or elaborate. The necessary items include: shelter for instruments, thermometers, barometer, hygrometer, wind vane, anemometer (wind speed indicator), and a rain gauge.

Shelter

If conditions permit, in the area of the station, a shelter to house observational instruments should be built. Anyone who has visited a weather station has seen the simple shelter provided for professional work. It consists of a wooden rectangular enclosure whose sides and top are louvered like wooden shutters. It should be of a size to hold easily all the instruments planned to be housed—if doubt exists about how large to make it, remember it is better too large than too small. Ventilation is necessary to allow free air circulation around the instruments while not permitting sunlight to strike them directly. The enclosure should be five or more feet above the ground so that the earth's effect on temperature and other measurements is reduced and the observer can read the instruments in a normal standing position. The shelter should have, of course, one hinged side to serve as a door. Preferably the hinges should be at the top so the door swings out and up, still protecting instruments from the rays of the sun. When it is completed, the shelter should be painted white to reflect as much of the sun's light as possible. The shelter should be placed away from buildings, thirty feet or more if this is practicable so that reflected sunlight from large walls and heat from buildings during the winter will not influence the observations.

Thermometer

The most common weather question that arises among people who are not intensely interested in skywatching is: What's the temperature today? This fundamental bit of information plays an important part in the meteorologist's measurements and is, fortunately, answered quite easily within allowable limits of accuracy.

Mercury or alcohol thermometers are those in widest use throughout the country and these, fortunately, are not too expensive. Of course, the more accurate mercury thermometers used by professionals are more costly but even they are not without error. Readings accurate to within a degree are acceptable and even cheap thermometers, when used correctly, can give such accuracy. One way to compensate for the errors in cheap thermometers is to purchase three or four of them, mount them on a single piece of wood and average their readings at each observation.

Reading temperatures is not quite so simple as it may seem at first thought. Even the most expensive mercury thermometer requires calibration from time to time and all must be handled carefully. A quick check on the accuracy of any thermometer can be made by immersing the entire instrument in a mixture of ice and water which has been allowed to stand until the water has reached equilibrium temperature with the ice, namely 32°. If the thermometer after being in the mixture a few moments reads 33° at its lowest, then you know the thermometer "reads high" by one degree. You can make a one-degree correction when the thermometer is put to actual use.

The operating principle of the mercury thermometer is the known expansion of the liquid mercury or alcohol with a rise in temperature. To make the expansion noticeable over a small temperature range, the liquid reservoir in the bulb at the bottom is open to a small capillary tube in the glass. Thus when the liquid expands, it rises in the tube. Materials such as mercury are surprisingly sensitive to temperature change. A good example of their sensitivity is watching the mercury rise in the capillary tube when the bulb is held in your hand. From an air temperature of, say, 72°F, the rise to body temperature of 98.6°F is rapid. In fact, in reading the thermometer within the shelter, a skywatcher should stand as far from the thermometer as possible and downwind of it to keep his own body heat from affecting the reading. Ideally, a thermometer should be suspended from a swivel or long cord so, before reading it, an observer can twirl it several times and makes certain it is registering the temperature of a moving supply of the air.

Any well-equipped station should have maximum and minimum thermometers. The maximum thermometer has a slight constriction in the small capillary tube. When the mercury expands and rises through that constriction it cannot return and thus remains at a level that shows the maximum temperature between times of observation. It is like a clinical thermometer used by doctors and nurses which must be shaken vigorously to get the mercury down through the constricted passage.

The minimum thermometer uses alcohol instead of mercury. It has a small float in the capillary which goes down as the alcohol contracts and lowers in the tube. When the temperature begins to rise, however, the float sticks against the glass at the lowest point and the alcohol flows by leaving the float to indicate the minimum reading between observation times. In some minimum thermometers the float is magnetized and can be drawn again to the top of the column by the use of a small permanent magnet. In other types the float is returned to the top of the column by inverting the thermometer and allowing the force of gravity to move it.

Electrical thermometers are in wide use and while they can

be purchased, they also can be built by anyone having an interest in and knowledge of a few simple electrical principles. The simplest type and one which can be arranged to be read at some distance from the shelter uses the principle that electrical resistance in a wire changes with the temperature of the wire. As the temperature rises, the resistance to the flow of an electrical current rises. Using a simple Wheatstone bridge circuit—an electrical circuit to measure resistances of wires very accurately—the observer adjusts the circuit until it is balanced and then reads the temperature from the variable rheostat used to balance the bridge. The rheostat, of course, is calibrated to read in degrees Fahrenheit. Details for its construction can be found in many texts on meteorological instruments.

Still another type makes use of the principle of the expansion of metals with an increase in temperature. Two dissimilar metals welded or brazed together form what is called a bimetallic strip. Since they expand at different rates as the temperature changes, the strip tends to bend. If it is in the form of a coil, it either tightens or uncoils a little with changes in temperature. This action is transmitted to a dial by means of a system of springs and levers and a hand which magnifies the motion so the dial can be read. Many thermostats and most dial type thermometers make use of this idea.

A continuously recording thermometer which keeps track of minute-by-minute changes is the ultimate in observational recording. Called a thermograph, it operates on the principle of the bimetallic strip as do the dial thermometers. But the indicating hand has a small point at one end connected to a reservoir of ink. As the hand moves it traces a record of the temperature changes on a piece of specially marked graph paper placed usually on a slowly rotating drum. Some of the thermograph drums are hand wound like a clock and are spring driven. More elaborate ones are electrically driven by a small motor.

Whatever type thermometer is chosen by an observer he must take care to reduce errors in his readings due to carelessness. To summarize, he should (a) check his thermometer or thermometers against more accurate ones or calibrate it by exposing it to known temperatures; (b) allow air to flow over the bulb during reading; (c) keep it protected from the sunlight; (d) stand as far away downwind of it when reading it as possible; (e) remember to read it with his line of sight making as nearly as possible an angle of 90 degrees with the glass tube, for if he views it on some other angle his line of sight will give him an apparent higher or lower reading than exists; (f) periodically check all types of thermometers for accuracy because handling and the mere passage of time can put them off.

Barometer

Pressure changes in the atmosphere also are important for the meteorologist to know and to note these changes he uses a barometer which is one of two types: mercurial or aneroid.

Of the two, the aneroid is the most convenient for the hobbyist's use. It is the type most commonly encountered and consists of a flat, partially evacuated tin can with a corrugated top. As the pressure of the atmosphere changes the relatively large area of the top moves in or out. The principle can be demonstrated by pressing on the sides of an empty, rectangular gallon can. The metal flexes in response to your pressure and returns to its original position when the pressure is removed. Though the motion of the aneroid "can" is small, it is magnified through a system of levers and springs so that a moving hand indicates the pressure on a properly marked dial.

Though not so accurate as the mercury barometer, the aneroid is sufficiently exact for most purposes and does not require the care and adjustment necessary for the mercury barometer. All that must be done to read the aneroid, is to tap the glass cover gently with one finger to bring the hand to its true resting point and then note the pressure.

Most inexpensive aneroid barometers show pressure in the usual inches of mercury. Some have an additional scale so the pressure may be read in millimeters of mercury. But the unit used by professional skywatchers is millibars. This unit is actually the familiar 14.7 lbs. per square inch translated into the metric absolute system of measurement and becomes dynes per square centimeter. Standard atmospheric pressure using this system is 1013.6 millibars where 1000 millibars represents a million dynes per square centimeter. Since most pressure data discussions among meteorologists involve millibars, the amateur might just as well keep his records in the approved unit.

To convert either inches of mercury or millimeters of mercury to millibars, the hobbyist can consult tables in meteorological texts or use the following information to construct his own:

The standard sea-level pressure of 29.92 inches of mercury equals 760 millimeters of mercury which equals 1013.6 millibars. Changes in pressure are directly proportional in any system of units. Thus if the pressure should rise 10 millimeters of mercury, the corresponding millibar reading would be 770/760 times 1013.6 millibars. If it fell one inch (a very large change but used to illustrate the method of conversion), the millibar reading would be 1013.6 x 28.92/29.92.

The mercury barometer is, of course, the classic pressure-measuring instrument and is based on the fact that the normal pressure of the atmosphere will, at sea level, uphold a column of the liquid metal to a height of 29.92 inches or 760 millimeters. The disadvantages of the mercury barometer are many, however. It must be carefully adjusted before being read and a correction for temperature must be made. To make a mercury barometer is possible but it entails very delicate manipulation and the amateur may well find himself with a pool of spilled mercury at considerable expense since the metal is expensive. On top of this any mercury that is spilled is hard to retrieve and its vapor is extremely poisonous. So probably the best instrument is the aneroid. It can be checked against a mercury barometer at a local weather station from time to time and calibrated to give satisfactory results.

A recording barometer is called a barograph and, like the thermograph, keeps a running record on a special graph of the pressure changes. The aneroid type barometer is used to make barographs and the rotating drum may either be spring driven or electrically driven as was the case in the thermograph.

Weather station readings of pressure all are reduced to "sea level" for comparison. This is necessary because there is a normal reduction of atmospheric pressure as altitude above sea level increases. Thus Denver, Colorado, would have less pressure at its nearly mile-high location than Houston, Texas. To draw synoptic charts, then, all pressure data must be adjusted. The hobbyist, however, need not do this unless he wishes to compare his observation with that of other stations. What he is primarily interested in is the change in pressure and the speed of that change in his locality.

Hygrometer

Every sample of air taken from the atmosphere contains some water vapor. The entrance and exit of this vapor from the other constituents of the atmosphere is a never-ending part of the weather cycle. Over oceans and large lakes, evaporation of water sends the molecules into the air. Warm air can hold much more water vapor than cold, and when moist, warm air is cooled sufficiently, the water vapor condenses and leaves the atmosphere in the form of clouds, fog, rain or snow. Meteorologists measure the amount of water vapor in the atmosphere with a hygrometer. There are two usual methods of measuring the humidity, as it is termed. The first is called absolute humidity and refers to the actual weight of water vapor in a given weight or mass of air. The second and most common method of stating the matter is by using what is known as relative humidity. This tells the observer the ratio, expressed as a percentage figure, of the amount of water vapor in the air compared with the amount of vapor the air could hold at that temperature. If, for example, the air contains half of what it could hold at the current temperature, the relative humidity would be described as 50 per cent.

The direct reading hygrometer, usually encased, has a hand which moves over a dial marked off in per cent so the observer can tell at a glance what the relative humidity is. Many substances expand when they are moist and contract when they dry out. Human hair is such a material and, surprisingly, many hygrometers make use of a single long human hair to function.

Such instruments can be purchased but if a hobbyist wants to make a humidity measuring instrument he had best settle for a sling psychrometer. This consists, essentially, of two thermometers mounted on a piece of plywood or light metal. One end of the frame is connected by a swivel fastening to a handle. The bulb or liquid reservoir of one of the thermometers is wrapped loosely with clean cotton or muslin cloth and the cloth is then soaked in clean water. The instrument is then swung rapidly about several times and the readings of the thermometers noted. Naturally the dry-bulb thermometer tells the air temperature. The wet-bulb thermometer reads noticeably lower. The reason for this is that the water on the cloth has evaporated at least partially, and in so doing has cooled the thermometer bulb. The amount of cooling depends on the rate of evaporation. The drier the air, the faster will water evaporate. So, the greater the difference between the two thermometer readings, the lower the humidity. To convert these thermometer readings into relative humidity requires a table of conversion numbers which can be found in many texts on meteorological instruments.

Human hair hygrometers sometimes are combined with thermographs to record the changes in relative humidity moment by moment and give the observer a running record. But these, like all recording instruments, are relatively expensive.

Wind Vane

The direction from which the wind comes tells much about current and expected weather. Wind, in fact, is a weather factor that for centuries has been acknowledged as a major weather indicator, and wind vanes of antique design are common sights on church steeples, barn roofs and houses. Good weather vanes can be purchased or made and they may be as elaborate or as simple as the hobbyist chooses. Perhaps the simplest that can be devised is a flag. If compass directions are painted at the base of the flagpole or cut from metal and mounted on the pole near the flag, a simple though not very accurate wind vane is the result.

The more usual type of wind vane, a rooster, ship or arrow cut from flat metal, and pivoted to swing above stationary cut-out compass points, can be constructed of light, weatherproof materials such as aluminum. The vane should be as free from the binding effects of friction as possible. This requirement points to the use of ball bearings but the hobbyist must keep in mind that most ball bearings and their housings are made of steel and will rust unless protected. Covering collars and frequent oiling will overcome this handicap.

Both flag and mechanical weather vanes suffer from the disadvantage that the observer must go outside to read them—unless they can be placed within sight of a window. Remote reading weather vanes can be constructed using a variety of ideas. Here is one that can easily be built. The key element is a car distributor, preferably from an older model eight cylinder car. The eight contact points of the distributor can be assigned the eight principal points of the compass and a simple electric circuit rigged to turn on one of eight bulbs arranged on a small display panel and suitably marked with compass abbreviations. The distributor, of course, must be mounted on the weather-vane shaft itself but the display panel can be as far away as necessary since only circuit wires must connect vane and panel. The circuit can be fitted with a switch so it is not using electric power continually but may be turned on and off when observations are taken. Using an electric train transformer will allow the hobbyist to plug directly into his house circuit. If the display panel is placed too far from such a power source, ordinary dry cells can be used in conjunction with mounted flashlight bulbs to give the wind indication.

Whatever the type of weather vane the hobbyist chooses he should take care where he mounts it. Ideally it should be high above the ground—twenty or more feet—and placed away from buildings. Air moving rapidly eddies and surges around corners of buildings and erratic if not erroneous wind-direction readings can result. If the vane is mounted on top of a building, place it as high above the roof on a pole as is practicable. The higher it is, the less will surges caused by air flowing up and over the building affect the readings.

Anemometer

Not only does the skywatcher want to know from what direction the wind is blowing he also wants to know its speed, or as it is sometimes referred to "force." To measure this weather factor any one of a number of kinds of anemometer can be employed. Like wind vanes, they can be simple or elaborate, homemade or purchased from a scientific instrument supply house.

In employing any kind of anemometer, it must be kept in mind that, like the wind vane, the location of the instrument is critical; it affects the accuracy of the observation. Like wind direction, wind speed has long been of interest to people—particularly sailors, pilots and meteorologists. Astute observation over the years shows that certain physical occurrences can give a measure of wind speed. Smoke rising straight up, of course, shows no wind at all. White caps breaking on a lake don't occur until the wind reaches a definite speed. Dust lifted, leaves blown, small tree branches bent, large limbs bent—all these have been used to estimate wind speed. In 1805 a British Admiral, Sir Francis Beaufort, devised a scale to estimate wind speed by visual means ranging from Force 0—calm—to Force 12—Hurricane speeds of more than 75 miles per hour. Still in use today the Beaufort Scale is about as accurate a visual estimation of wind speed as can be attained.

To take the guesswork out of wind-speed observation, meteorologists employ an anemometer usually of the cup type. The instrument consists of four hollow hemispheres fixed to spokes on a shaft. The cups spin at an increasing rate as the wind speed increases. At the other end of the rotating shaft are reducing gears which activate either an electric-light system, a buzzer system or a dial hand within the weather station. The carefully calibrated observation panel of such an anemometer will tell the observer at a glance exactly what the wind speed is.

Like most instruments accurate enough to satisfy professional meteorologists, the station anemometers are well designed and carefully constructed—which makes them expensive. Fortunately there are many other designs and ideas that can be used to construct a workable anemometer without spending too much money.

In all of them, of course, care must be taken to reduce effects of friction, protect gears and bearings from the weather and calibrate them carefully before installation as well as periodically while they are in use. In fact, as the hobbyist assembles his instruments, he would do well to become acquainted with the nearest weather station employees, many of whom will gladly allow him to check his instruments against the station's professionally built and maintained measuring devices.

Here, briefly, are a number of ideas that can be used to produce anemometers. They range from the very simplest, to more elaborate ones.

The plate anemometer is perhaps the least expensive either to buy or build. It consists of a flat plate of light metal or plywood held lightly at one end in bronze or brass pivot bearings. A semicircular scale is fastened to the frame so that when the anemometer is held facing the wind and the pivoted plate swings in response to the force of the moving air, the observer can read the wind speed on the calibrated scale. Several companies that produce educational toys and equipment have plastic plate anemometers on the market.

Another simple type anemometer makes use of an automobile speedometer and a propeller attached to the speedometer shaft. The speedometer can be fitted with a handle and the anemometer would then be a manual type, or the propeller can be mounted atop a pole with the flexible shaft running down to the speedometer. Of course, for measuring wind speeds with a propeller some adjustment will have to be made on the speedometer. In this type instrument the effects of friction must be carefully considered.

Yet another type which makes use of revolving cups employs a car distributor on which all but one of the contact bumps has been ground off. Like the wind vane, it makes use of electrical contact to flash a light or sound a buzzer for the observation. Cups for this anemometer can be made from soldered galvanized metal cones or any hollow metal spheres cut in half. Remember, however, that the cups will be exposed continuously to the weather and should be of metal that will not corrode easily. A reducing gear mechanism will have to be employed on this type—otherwise the speed of rotation would give almost uncountably rapid flashes of light at the observation panel. Once again, when employing any type reducing gear, be certain to make it as free from friction as possible. If reducing gears are not to the hobbyist's liking, he can use friction wheels—a small one connected to the anemometer cup shaft pressing against a larger wheel which would turn its shaft more slowly.

Perhaps one of the simplest and most accurate home-built types available makes use of the wooden propeller, a flexible shaft and a small revolution counter which has its own gear reducing mechanism. Whenever an observation is desired, the hobbyist presses the revolution counter against the end of the rotating flexible shaft and determines the number of revolutions per minute. With a calibration chart which he can make, he can then interpret the rpms in terms of miles per hour.

Another electrical type can be made from a simple, toy electric generator. If this machine is connected to either spinning anemometer cups or a propeller shaft, the generated voltage is directly proportional to the speed of the turning armature. A voltmeter of the proper range then calibrated in miles per hour will provide the reading instrument.

Rain Gauge

One of the simplest yet most important weather measurements is that of precipitation. Even the professional instrument for its measurement is not expensive. The gauge is nothing more than two metal containers, a funnel top and a wooden stick with a scale on it. The principle is simple: catch the water and measure the amount that fell. To measure slight amounts of precipitation, however, is difficult with, say, an ordinary drum or bucket. Hence the inner and outer container and the funnel. The funnel (preferably with a vertical lip around it) fits snugly over the top of the larger, outside container. The smaller inner container receives the water. Carefully made, the funnel top is just ten times as large in area as the cross section area of the small inner container. Thus a small amount of rain is magnified by a factor of ten when it rises in the small container. The measuring stick, marked in inches, might read one inch of water in the inner container which would indicate that one-tenth of an inch of rain had fallen.

Rain gauges can be purchased inexpensively or made. While ratios other than one to ten can be employed, whatever is used must be multiplied by the observed water depth to determine inches of rainfall. If the hobbyist makes a rain gauge or has one made, he should use noncorrosive metal such as aluminum or copper.

Snowfall measurement even for the expert is a difficult task. Wind-driven snow drifts in some places and is blown from others. To discover how much has fallen, meteorologists use a long pole and determine the depth at several places where it has apparently neither drifted nor blown clear. An average is then taken and that average is reduced to its equivalent depth of water. Even this method contains some error since some types of snow have more water than others. As an average figure, the hobbyist can use ten inches of snow being equivalent to one inch of water. The only other way to make this measurement is to take several core samples of snow that has recently fallen, allow it to melt and see just how many inches of snow produce an inch of water. If, for example, a one foot tube is pressed firmly into the snow and the core allowed to melt, it might reduce to one inch of water. This, then would be the equivalence ratio for that particular snowfall. The outer container of the rain gauge can be used for this purpose. Several samples should be taken and the results averaged to remove errors insofar as possible.

Of course, rainfall in a region is an important piece of climatic data and the beginning skywatcher can find plenty of enjoyment keeping records of rainfall in his own area as a start, if the cost of other instruments prohibits him from operating a full-fledged station with all its attendant observations. But when he begins to keep records of this and other measurements the hobbyist should proceed in the simplest, most orderly fashion possible to make his data available to him at a glance.

Records

The hourly recording of surface data at a weather station is made on a form that includes the following information:

Station pressure, dry-bulb thermometer reading, wet-bulb reading, relative humidity (from the conversion chart), total sky cover—recorded in tenths, description of lowest and subsequently higher cloud layers if visible which includes amount of coverage, type of cloud, direction of motion and estimated height, present tendency of the weather and the net three-hour change. There is space for recording the corrections made in the station pressure to convert it to sea level and correct it for temperature variation.

On each daily page of the hobbyist's log or workbook he should leave space for remarks, summarization of the general weather characteristics and the notation of unusual phenomena. He might also, if he is brave, note how near his forecast for a previous period came to the mark.

If weather is a hobby, hourly records of data, of course, are scarcely possible. Even the desirable four observations daily may not be obtainable for they should be taken at 7:30 A.M., 1:30 P.M., 7:30 P.M. and 1:30 A.M. At best, the hobbyist may make the morning and early-evening observations but if this is not possible he will have to settle for one a day. Nonetheless, over a period of time, he will collect a formidable array of data that will be a true running record of the weather.

In making his observations, the observer can scarcely pay too much attention to clouds (see p. 61), for with knowledge of the clouds alone he could begin to make surprisingly good forecasts of what the weather will be in his locality. As his knowledge of local eccentricities of weather builds up he can increase the accuracy of his forecasts. Not the least important facet of cloud observation is that his instruments record only the surface data—and much weather lies above the surface. Clouds give him his only clue to the upper-air goings on. Skill in cloud interpretation will augment instrument reading so that by interpreting both clouds and instruments the hobbyist will begin to appreciate the endlessly absorbing art of forecasting the weather.

Professional skywatchers always are interested in the amateur and so conscious is the Weather Bureau of the interest of thousands of people in weather study that the Bureau makes available, at very little cost, weather maps on a subscription basis, bulletins and booklets that not only give the latest extended forecast from the National Meteorological Center but also instruction in the art of forecasting—that prime art of skywatchers. Inquiries directed to the Weather Bureau are welcomed by the men concerned with disseminating information to the public. Like all such endeavors, however, it requires some organization and basic rules. If the hobbyist will follow the Bureau's instructions in ordering material, he soon will have a growing library on the weather and daily or weekly information to help him.

Whether professional or amateur, skywatchers the world around have discovered that this ocean of air we live in offers a lifetime of study. It affects our lives, our fortunes and our moods. It is both grand and subtle, beautiful and powerful—and without its presence we cannot exist on the planet called earth.

Index

j551.5
Bi
Bixby, William   DISCARD

     Skywatchers   1962

21669

DATE DUE

MEMORIAL PUBLIC LIBRARY
ALEXANDRIA, PENNA.

RULES

1. Books may be kept two weeks and may be renewed once for the same period, except 7 day books and magazines.

2. A fine of two cents a day will be charged on each book which is not returned according to the above rule. No book will be issued to any person incurring such a fine until it has been paid.

3. All injuries to books beyond reasonable wear and all losses shall be made good to the satisfaction of the Librarian.

4. Each borrower is held responsible for all books drawn on his card and for all fines accruing on the same.